The Essential Anti-Anxiety Handbook
© 2024 Future Publishing Limited

Future Books is an imprint of Future PLC
Quay House, The Ambury, Bath, BA1 1UA

A catalogue record for this book is
available from the British Library.

ISBN 978-1-80521-763-3 hardback

The paper holds full FSC certification
and accreditation.

Printed in Turkey by Ömür Printing, for Future PLC

**Interested in Foreign Rights to publish this title?
Email us at:**
licensing@futurenet.com

Group Editor
Philippa Grafton

Senior Designer
Briony Duguid

Contributors
**Edoardo Albert, Julie Bassett, Dr Sinead Doyle,
Scott Dutfield, Ben Grafton, Emma Green,
Ailsa Harvey, Trisha Lewis, Laura Mears,
Sara Niven, Lauren Scott, Jacqueline Snowden,
Sharon Walker**

Senior Art Editor
Andy Downes

Head of Art & Design
Greg Whitaker

Editorial Director
Jon White

Managing Director
Grainne McKenna

Production Project Manager
Matthew Eglinton

Global Business Development Manager
Jennifer Smith

Senior International Trade Marketing Associate
Kate Waldock

Head of Future International & Bookazines
Tim Mathers

Cover images
Getty Images

Future plc is a public company
quoted on the London Stock
Exchange
(symbol: FUTR)
www.futureplc.com

Chief Executive Officer **Jon Steinberg**
Non-Executive Chairman **Richard Huntingford**
Chief Financial and Strategy Officer **Penny Ladkin-Brand**

Tel +44 (0)1225 442 244

MIX
Paper | Supporting
responsible forestry
FSC® C106499

The Essential
ANTI-ANXIETY
HANDBOOK

If you, or anyone you know, is affected by anxiety, the following charities and helplines are ready to offer free support.

The Essential
ANTI-ANXIETY
HANDBOOK

As attitudes towards mental health change and the pressures of everyday life increase, it's no surprise that more of us than ever before are suffering from anxiety. From worries that keep us up at night to crippling anxiety that leaves us housebound, none of us are immune to the stresses of life. But when does simple stress cross over into anxiousness? How bad do we need to feel before we take action? In this brand-new title, we reveal the effects that anxiety has on your brain and your body, as well as tips to help you manage day-to-day stresses. We also share expert advice on taking control of more intrusive anxiousness, including when to see a doctor and how CBT might change your outlook.

CONTENTS

THE SCIENCE OF ANXIETY

The brain's natural fear response evolved to keep our species safe, so what happens when it goes wrong?

WORDS LAURA MEARS

The word anxiety comes from the Latin 'angere', which literally means 'to choke'. It describes the feeling of physical and emotional unease we experience when anticipating a threat. It has been critical to our success as a species, making us feel uncomfortable in the face of danger for thousands of years.

The purpose of anxiety is adaptation. It prepares us to fight or flee if possible, or freeze in place if not. It initiates rapid activation of the sympathetic nervous system, a network of nerves that reach into every corner of the body. These nerves spit out a chemical called noradrenaline, also known as norepinephrine. Related to adrenaline, this chemical initiates a wave of changes that prepare the mind and

"SIDE EFFECTS INCLUDE NAUSEA, DIZZINESS, HOT FLUSHES AND IRRITABILITY"

body for physical action. The heart rate rises, the breathing quickens, the blood vessels in the muscles dilate, and the mind becomes hyper alert.

Researchers disagree about whether anxiety and fear are the same. They both alert us to danger and trigger similar protective biological responses. But, while the focus of fear is often external danger, the focus of anxiety can be anything, physical or psychological, real or hypothetical. In times of physical danger, the changes the fight or flight response triggers are essential. But, often in the case of anxiety, the source of the threat is less tangible.

When there is nothing to fight against or flee from, the physical fear reaction can feel very unpleasant. Side effects include nausea, tingling, dizziness, hot flushes, restlessness, trouble concentrating, irritability, and a feeling often described as an unshakeable sense of dread.

Anxiety disorders
Many people experience cycles of anxious thoughts and feelings that become so intense that they start to impact their everyday lives. This is when normal human anxiety becomes an anxiety disorder. This group of psychiatric conditions can be acute or chronic, lasting a short amount of time or persisting for years. There are many types, ranging from generalised anxiety and panic attacks to phobias and obsessive compulsive disorder. Doctors have known

THE ANXIETY RESPONSE

CORTEX
The brain's information-processing areas trigger anxious feelings, consciously or subconsciously.

Ⓐ AMYGDALA
The fear centre senses danger and initiates the fight or flight response.

LATERAL PERIAQUEDUCTAL GRAY
The amygdala sends signals to the lateral periaqueductal gray, which tells the muscles to prepare for action.

HYPOTHALAMUS
The amygdala contacts the hypothalamus, telling it to switch on the sympathetic nervous system.

PITUITARY GLAND
The hypothalamus sends chemical messages to the pituitary gland, which starts pumping hormones into the blood.

ADRENAL GLANDS
Hormones from the pituitary gland arrive at the adrenal glands, telling them to make the stress hormone cortisol.

SYMPATHETIC NERVOUS SYSTEM
The sympathetic nervous system releases noradrenaline, and the adrenal glands release adrenaline, two major fight or flight chemicals.

Ⓑ HEART AND LUNGS
The body responds by increasing the heart rate, quickening the breathing, and diverting blood to the muscles.

THE EFFECTS OF ANXIETY

❶ PALPITATIONS
Adrenaline ramps up the heart rate, causing the heart to pound or flutter in the chest.

❷ BREATHLESSNESS
The muscles scream for oxygen as the body prepares to fight or flee, causing a sensation of breathlessness.

❸ HOT FLUSHES
The blood vessels widen to deliver more oxygen to the muscles, making the skin feel hot.

❹ SWEATING
The nervous system triggers sweating in the hands, feet, face and armpits.

❺ NAUSEA
Blood moves away from the intestines and the muscles slow down causing cramping and nausea.

❻ DIARRHOEA
Contractions in the large intestine speed up to empty the bowel.

❼ TREMBLING
The muscles prepare to jump into action, and become twitchy and overexcited.

❽ PANIC
The physical symptoms feed back to the brain, magnifying feelings of restlessness and panic.

WHAT CAUSES PANIC ATTACKS?

Panic attacks can start without warning, flooding the body with a wave of physical symptoms that seem to have come from nowhere. But these events don't happen totally out of the blue. Researchers at Southern Methodist University have shown that signs of an impending panic attack can begin up to an hour beforehand. Monitoring people with panic disorder revealed that, in the run-up to a panic attack, blood carbon dioxide levels start to fall. Then, just before the panic attack begins, they suddenly rise. This makes the brain think that it is suffocating, triggering feelings of intense fear. The link between carbon dioxide and panic attacks might explain why slow, deep breathing is such an effective treatment. It helps to restore the body back to its normal balance.

about anxiety disorders for centuries. The father of medicine, Hippocrates, described a man called Nicanor, who had a phobia of the flute more than 2,000 years ago. Hearing the sound of the instrument would cause him intense anxiety. At the time, there was no diagnosis and no treatment. Clinical understanding of anxiety has improved dramatically over the centuries, but it wasn't until relatively recently that the biology of fear, panic and anxiety started to become clear.

One of the first researchers to investigate anxiety was Ivan Pavlov. The physiologist noticed strange behaviour in his animals after a traumatic event. In September 1924, a storm flooded St Petersburg. Pavlov's dog kennels were submerged. To escape the rising water, the dogs

The amygdala (red) is part of the brain's limbic system and plays a key role in processing emotions

had to swim to the laboratory on the floor above. They endured terrifying sights and sounds on their journey, including lashing rain, crashing waves and falling trees. After the storm subsided, some dogs returned to their training as though nothing had happened. But others became troubled and withdrawn. Writing about one of the dogs, Pavlov explained, "The animal was abnormally restless and all conditioned reflexes were practically absent... the animal now would not touch the food". This dog was experiencing post-traumatic stress disorder. All the staff could do to reassure it and restore its normal behaviour was to keep it company.

Why only some of the dogs developed anxiety after the flood is a big question in anxiety research.

Individuals can experience the same life events and emerge with completely different psychological reactions; they seem to have their own thresholds for anxiety disorder development. It is likely that these thresholds are influenced by genetics.

Genetic causes

The centre of the brain's fear response is a pair of walnut-sized structures called the amygdala. This cellular

"RECENTLY, THE BIOLOGY OF FEAR, PANIC AND ANXIETY BECAME CLEAR"

junction box communicates across the brain. It receives inputs from the sensory system, keeping a constant watch for signs of danger. If it detects a problem, it sends signals to the hypothalamus and the brain stem, which activate the fight or flight response.

One of the brain areas that sends signals into the amygdala is a group of cells called the raphe nuclei. These cells send out the feel-good brain chemical serotonin. This chemical has gained a reputation for being the 'happy hormone', but its role in anxiety is not so positive.

A group of antidepressants called selective serotonin reuptake inhibitors (SSRIs) help to improve mood by keeping serotonin around in the brain for longer, but they can also increase

anxiety. Researchers at the University of North Carolina Healthcare wanted to understand why, so they tracked the activity of serotonin nerves in the brains of mice. They traced serotonin-induced anxiety back to a group of cells that connect the raphe nuclei to a brain area called the 'bed nucleus of the stria terminalis'.

Sometimes known as the 'extended amygdala', this brain area links the parts of the brain that sense danger with the parts of the brain that trigger a response. Serotonin signals here change the messages that reach the brain's fight or flight switchboard, the hypothalamus. When serotonin levels increase, the hypothalamus flips the parasympathetic nervous system 'off', and the sympathetic nervous system 'on'. This causes anxiety to rise.

Changes to the serotonin signalling system appear frequently in studies searching for the genetic causes of anxiety. Researchers have identified mutations in several serotonin-related genes that appear to increase the risk of anxiety disorders. These include the genes for the receptor that detects serotonin, the transporter that clears it away, and the enzyme that breaks it down.

Some individuals with these genetic changes even have visible differences inside their brains. Scans have shown that genetic differences in serotonin signalling can alter the connections between the amygdala and a part of the brain called the fusiform gyrus, which is responsible for face detection.

Another group of brain chemicals that play a role in anxiety are the catecholamines. These include the fight or flight chemicals adrenaline and noradrenaline (also known as epinephrine and norepinephrine). Nerves that make noradrenaline start in a part of the brain called the locus coeruleus, or 'blue spot', which communicates with the amygdala. It has a powerful role to play in

DO ANIMALS GET ANXIOUS?

The brain chemistry that triggers anxiety evolved because it is essential for our survival. The pathways that drive our overactive fear response are the same ones that underpin our ability to sense and respond to real threats. We share those pathways with all other mammals, making it likely that they are capable of experiencing anxiety too. It's hard for scientists to measure anxiety in animals because they can't tell us how they're feeling. But their behaviour can be a giveaway. In dogs, for example, separation from a trusted owner can trigger the same kinds of physical anxiety symptoms seen in humans. They become agitated, their muscles tremble, and they can be sick or lose control of their bowels. Treatment for anxiety in animals is similar, too. It involves making them feel safe, providing distractions during distressing situations, and seeking professional support when it becomes too much to manage at home.

vigilance and attention, and it helps to tune incoming sensory signals.

Nerve impulses from the locus coeruleus dial up the amygdala's fear response. They instruct the fear centre to send messages to the hypothalamus that tell it to release a chemical called corticotropin-releasing hormone. This tells the brain's pituitary gland to release a hormone that prepares the body for incoming stress. Researchers at Boston Children's Hospital found that blocking corticotropin-releasing hormone makes cautious mice fearless. They visit brightly lit areas, walk across narrow planks, and don't hesitate to investigate strange new objects.

Environmental factors

Not everyone with alterations in their genetic makeup will go on to develop anxiety. Genetics might determine a person's underlying threshold for developing a particular anxiety disorder, but life events determine whether that threshold will ever be breached.

Research has shown that anxiety disorders rarely occur on their own. In fact, 60-90% of people with anxiety also have another mental health condition. This might be depression, substance misuse or another type of anxiety disorder. Sometimes one disorder directly causes another. Other times, several disorders have the same underlying causes, making people likely to develop them in combination.

Treatments

The frontline treatment for those struggling is cognitive behavioural therapy (CBT), a talking therapy that helps people learn to break out of cycles of negative thoughts. It encourages people to look closely at the connections between their thoughts, feelings, physical sensations and actions.

According to researchers at the Norwegian University of Science and Technology, CBT is far more effective than medication for treating anxiety. Drug treatments might dampen the physical and psychological symptoms, but the effects are often only temporary. CBT addresses negative thought patterns directly. In a trial that compared the two types of treatment, 85% of participants improved using CBT alone.

One of the challenges in treating anxiety is the amount of time it takes for people to come forward and ask for help. According to a paper published in Nature Reviews, it often takes between three and 30 years. But research has also shown that asking for help early can make anxiety easier to manage.

ANXIETY
DISORDERS

The distinction between 'normal' levels of anxiety and intrusive, detrimental thoughts can be difficult to make. We look at the most common disorders associated with anxiety and try to understand how they might be negatively influencing our daily lives

WORDS BEN GRAFTON

From worrying about credit card bills, to starting a new job, or even becoming a parent for the first time, anxiety inevitably affects all of us at some point in our lives. The advantages of living and working in a 24/7 inter-connected world are often offset by our inability to switch off from life's demands, and the physiological symptoms are all too familiar: a racing pulse, clammy palms, and that constricting or crushing sensation in our chest. Anxiety can be easy to dismiss as we fail to recognise the unhelpful thought patterns that precede it.

While feelings of worry are part of being human, one in six adults regularly struggle with common mental health problems, such as anxiety or depression, which impact negatively on their daily life. This leads to avoidant behaviours, problems such as sleep difficulties and potentially impacts on both professional and personal relationships. If you recognise that anxiety is negatively influencing your life, you might be living with an anxiety disorder.

It is important to recognise that anxiety disorders can go hand-in-hand with other mental health conditions and disorders. Many of these are treatable, but there is often not a 'one size fits all' solution. For example, anti-anxiety medications, such as selective serotonin reuptake inhibitors (or SSRIs), might be a godsend for some, while for others mindfulness or cognitive behavioural therapies (which 'retrain' the brain to process stressful emotions) might be far more effective.

If you are struggling with anxiety it is therefore important to seek expert advice, whether from your GP or a qualified mental health professional, to get to the root cause and find a treatment that works best for you, so that you can keep on living your best life.

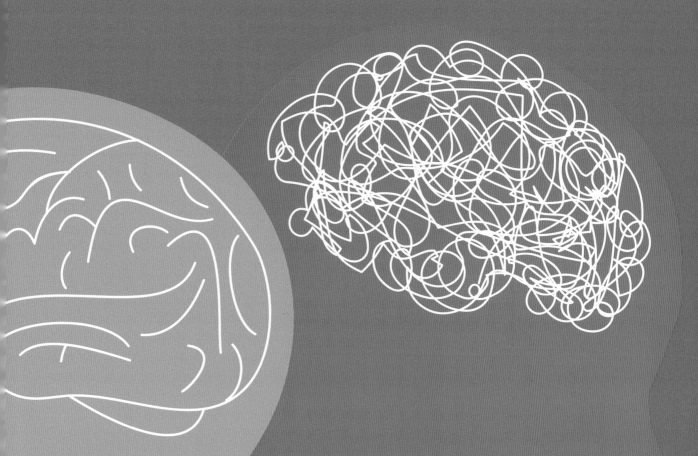

"IF YOU'RE
STRUGGLING
WITH ANXIETY IT IS
IMPORTANT TO SEEK
EXPERT ADVICE"

GENERALISED ANXIETY DISORDER (GAD)

The 'catch-all' condition

By far the most common anxiety disorder is generalised anxiety disorder (GAD). Affecting up to 5% of the UK population, it is characterised by persistent and pervasive feelings of anxiety about a range of subjects, often based on unrealistic or extreme 'worst-case' outcomes. Common symptoms include restlessness, insomnia and heart palpitations. If you've got GAD you might not be able to remember the last time you did not feel anxious. Reasons for this vary, and might be attributed to anything from an imbalance of brain chemicals, genetics, or as a result of previous life experiences.

For a typical GAD sufferer, mundane things like long-distance road trips can trigger fears of a fatal road accident, while social occasions might cause premonitions of complete social embarrassment and scorn. In short, no subject is off the table when it comes to creating unnecessary worry.

"FOR A TYPICAL GAD SUFFERER, MUNDANE THINGS CAN TRIGGER FEARS"

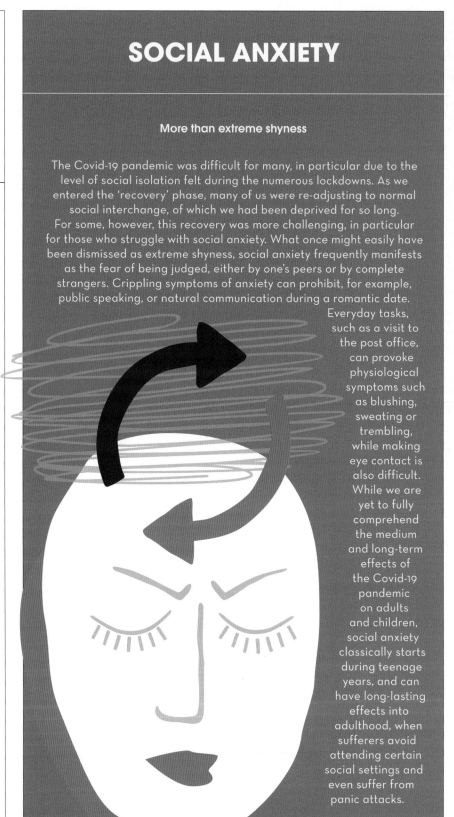

SOCIAL ANXIETY

More than extreme shyness

The Covid-19 pandemic was difficult for many, in particular due to the level of social isolation felt during the numerous lockdowns. As we entered the 'recovery' phase, many of us were re-adjusting to normal social interchange, of which we had been deprived for so long. For some, however, this recovery was more challenging, in particular for those who struggle with social anxiety. What once might easily have been dismissed as extreme shyness, social anxiety frequently manifests as the fear of being judged, either by one's peers or by complete strangers. Crippling symptoms of anxiety can prohibit, for example, public speaking, or natural communication during a romantic date.

Everyday tasks, such as a visit to the post office, can provoke physiological symptoms such as blushing, sweating or trembling, while making eye contact is also difficult. While we are yet to fully comprehend the medium and long-term effects of the Covid-19 pandemic on adults and children, social anxiety classically starts during teenage years, and can have long-lasting effects into adulthood, when sufferers avoid attending certain social settings and even suffer from panic attacks.

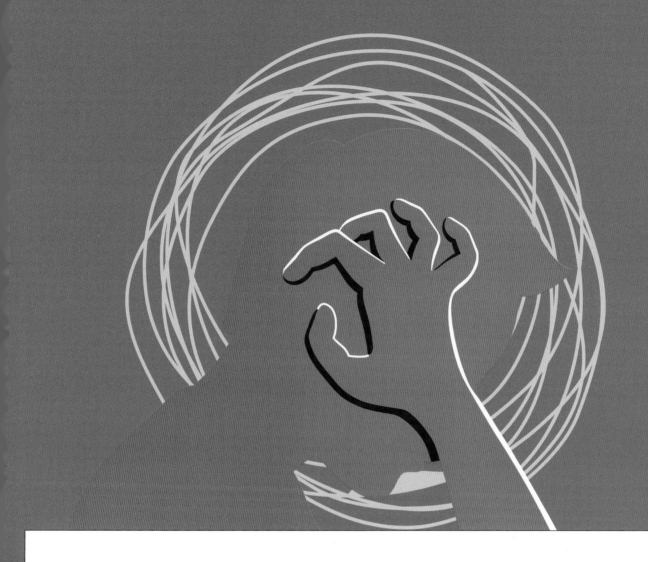

POST-TRAUMATIC STRESS DISORDER (PTSD)

The fallout from trauma

Post-traumatic stress disorder (PTSD) is an anxiety disorder that is triggered by a traumatic event, either experienced or witnessed. It was first recognised in soldiers during World War I, who presented with post-traumatic symptoms labelled as 'shell shock'. As well as survivors of war, victims of violence and sexual assault, traumatic accidents and grief can experience PTSD, and it is recognised that first responders and members of the emergency services are also at risk.

Symptoms of PTSD include flashbacks, nightmares and severe anxiety, including panic attacks, and the diagnosis is usually made where these symptoms persist for over a month. Sufferers may experience feelings of persistent irritability and hyperarousal, and may demonstrate behaviours which seek to avoid the trigger or other stressful settings.

AGORAPHOBIA

No way out

In ancient Greece, the 'Agora' was a public area intended for meetings or gatherings, which is why agoraphobia is commonly believed to be the fear of crowded spaces. However, more accurately, this anxiety disorder is characterised by a fear of being unable to escape, meaning that it can manifest anywhere from public transport to shops or simply leaving the comfort of your own home – something we can all relate to after the last two years.

Sufferers of agoraphobia experience anxiety and panic attacks which are triggered by certain situations. It is the avoidance of these situations that can eventually lead to more extreme forms, in which a person feels uncomfortable leaving their home. This can impact severely on a person's life, including their professional and financial situation, and for some, working from home is the only option.

If you think you might be experiencing symptoms and the thought of visiting your GP to discuss treatment options feels too difficult, help can be sought over the phone or online.

PANIC DISORDER

Fear of fear itself

Most people will experience a panic attack in their lifetime. This is defined by a short time period in which an overwhelming surge of anxiety is triggered, accompanied by symptoms such as a racing heartbeat, chest pain, trembling limbs and difficulty catching your breath. For many this is likely to be an infrequent or one-off event.

Panic disorder, however, is defined as having frequent panic attacks which are not attributed to a particular cause or trigger. It often leads to a fear of panic attacks themselves, and a vicious cycle of anxiety and worry. The causes can include biological or psychological factors.

Panic attacks can be alarming but they are not in themselves dangerous. However, they can evolve, to include, for example, agoraphobia, and can wreak havoc with a person's sense of wellbeing. It is therefore important to seek treatment if you think you might be affected.

PHOBIAS

Sweating the small stuff

Who hasn't experienced a phobia of some description? From the house spider that climbs up your bed in the middle of the night, to the waiting room jitters at the dentist? Those suffering from acute phobias might experience dizziness, nausea, trembling, and heart palpitations, making what might seem a trivial fear far more unnerving. While the fear is often exaggerated, the impact is real, and in some cases can be debilitating and cause misery to a person's life.

Phobias might begin after a traumatic event, and can be wide-ranging. They commonly include fear of animals, environmental factors such as heights, certain situations such as flying, or even bodily phobias, such as the fear of blood. However, what the medical profession refers to as 'simple phobias' can also be superseded by 'complex phobias', such as social phobia or agoraphobia. Depending on the type of phobia you have and how often you come into contact with it, the impact on daily life and subsequent need for treatment can vary greatly.

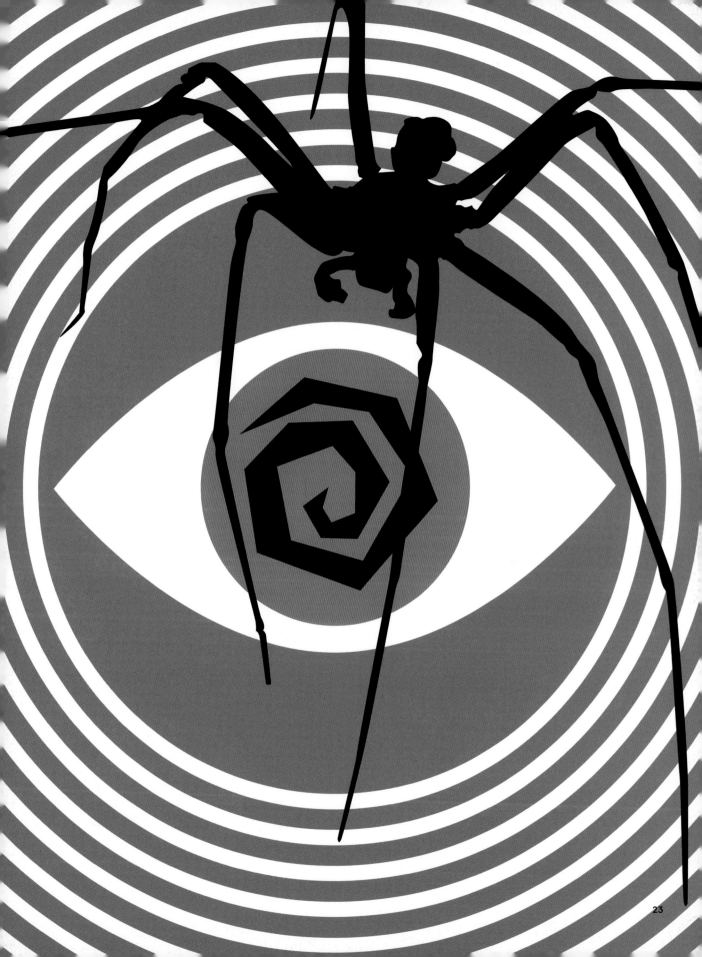

OBSESSIVE-COMPULSIVE DISORDER AND TOURETTE'S SYNDROME

"TICS ARE MOST COMMONLY SEEN IN CHILDREN AND YOUNG PEOPLE"

Commonly associated with anxiety

Obsessive-compulsive disorder (OCD) is closely associated with anxiety. It is a common disorder in which a person has uncontrollable, intruding recurring thoughts (obsessions) and/or repetitive behaviours (compulsions) that, when enacted, alleviate anxiety. Typically this might present as a fear of germs, leading to excessive cleaning and hand washing, or an obsession with order, leading to continuously rearranging or organising objects, for example. It is recognised that certain personality types, who prefer neatness and order, may have a propensity to develop this condition.

Tic disorders (known as 'Tourette's syndrome' where tics have been present for over a year) also have a strong association with anxiety. Tics are defined as sudden involuntary movements or vocalisations which are repetitive and unwanted. They can be defined as 'motor' tics, such as facial twitching, eye blinking or head or limb jerking, or as 'vocal' tics, which might include repetitive throat clearing, grunting or calling out. Sufferers of tics often describe a strong need to carry out the movement or noise before it happens, and a strong sense of relief once it is done. Tics are most commonly seen in children and young people, and for most, disappear by adulthood. While for many sufferers treatment is not needed, you should seek help if they are impacting significantly on your daily life.

EXPERT ADVICE

It is important to remember that anxiety overlaps with a host of other mental health and neurodevelopmental conditions, including depression and low mood, eating disorders, autism and ADHD (attention deficit hyperactivity disorder). It is therefore important to seek appropriate professional support if you are concerned.

THE
CYCLE *OF*
ANXIETY

*How the ancient foundations
of our brain can trap us
in anxiety in the present*

P
ity our poor brains. They evolved to deal with the challenges facing small bands of nomads in Africa. As nomads, we had to venture into unknown territories, climb over hills that no one had ever climbed before, swim across new rivers and venture into strange forests. Whenever we went into new, unfamiliar territory, our brains put themselves on high alert, drinking in all the information they could gather.

Entering alien lands, we were alive and alert, every sense stretching out, our minds picking up every cue. Was that the rustle of the wind through the grass or the stealthy movement of a lion, stalking us? Senses now on even higher alert, our ancestors spread out, signalling from one to the other as they moved around that thick clump of rustling grass, looking, looking…

It was just the wind. Even across the gulf of millennia we know exactly how our ancestors would have felt when they discovered there was nothing bad hiding behind the clump of grass: the sheer relief, the deep breaths, the stretching up and out. Smiles, laughs, maybe some ribaldry directed at the person who first called out, "Lion!"

That we know exactly how people who lived so long ago would have felt at this moment shows the deep, deep roots that feed anxiety, for our brains evolved to deal with the uncertainty of confronting new situations. Moving into new territories, our brains went on full alert, searching for anything that might prove dangerous to us or our tribe. But as we became familiar with the new territory, learning its geography and assessing it as safe, then our brains slowly relaxed. We became confident, secure. We could let the children play without having to keep them constantly in sight.

We could relax. Relaxation comes with the removal of uncertainty. As we became confident in a new territory, the uncertainty lessened until we felt secure… only for the herds to move on and the whole cycle of uncertainty and anxiety to begin again.

No one is saying that our ancestors had it easy. Few of us today have to

"ANY ACTION, NO MATTER HOW UNWISE, CAN MAKE YOU FEEL BETTER BY REDUCING ANXIETY LEVELS"

THE CYCLE OF ANXIETY

ANXIETY

Fear is natural. It is our quickest and deepest way to learn. But when fear is matched by uncertainty, it produces feelings of anxiety, as our brain desperately signals to us that it needs more information. It is telling us to do something. The feelings that accompany anxiety – sweating, heart beating fast, jitters – are its way of telling us that it is fearful but that it does not know what is going on.

AVOIDANCE

When our brain is telling us to do something to reduce the feelings of anxiety, we might sometimes decide to avoid what needs to be done. Physically avoiding an anxiety-producing situation, such as calling in sick rather than giving a talk, successfully removes the feelings. Or if we are feeling nervous about talking to new people at a party, a few drinks might enable us to overcome those feelings. We are on the way towards developing a habit.

ANXIETY

LONG-TERM ANXIETY GROWTH

ANXIETY CYCLE

AVOIDANCE

SHORT-TERM RELIEF FROM ANXIETY

LONG-TERM ANXIETY GROWTH

By developing behaviours that avoid our anxieties rather than facing and understanding the reason for these feelings, we increase our own sensitivity to feelings of anxiety. This makes it more likely we will resort to avoidance behaviour, embedding the pattern in our brains and in our lives. It can be very difficult to break this cycle.

SHORT-TERM RELIEF FROM ANXIETY

Having skipped the talk, we feel better. After a few drinks, we find our nervousness gone. Watching YouTube rather than writing that essay. All these behaviours – physical avoidance, alcohol, procrastination – reduce or remove the immediate feelings of anxiety. We have done something, as requested by our brain. But next time, we'll be more likely to use the same behaviours again, rather than facing our fears.

face the prospect of being attacked by a lion or an angry hippo. But our ancestors had one great advantage when it comes to anxiety: their worries were definite. It did not take long to see whether or not there was a leopard hiding up that tree. Our uncertainties are less defined and longer lasting. This is where the roots of anxiety lie.

Mental uncertainty provokes action. From an evolutionary point of view, the uncomfortable itch of uncertainty pushed us out of the cave to find out if that scratching noise was a bear or just a tree branch scraping against a rock. It's this urge to action produced by overwhelming uncertainty that explains the doomed teenager going back into the haunted house in a horror film: sometimes uncertainty

is so unsettling that any action, no matter how unwise, can actually make us feel better by reducing anxiety levels.

Anxiety and stress compel us to do something... anything.

The driver to these overwhelming feelings is the deepest, oldest part of our brains. We share these ancient systems with other animals because fear is the oldest driver of behaviour there is. You are exploring a cave. It's dark, quiet. Then something leaps out of the dark at you, roaring.

Standing, panting, outside the cave, you won't need to be reminded that this cave is the home of a rather grumpy bear. Nor will you ever again enter a dark cave without first checking that it's not

home to something nasty. Negative reinforcement is the oldest, most fundamental sort of learning. The sea slug, with its 20,000 neurons compared to a hundred billion for humans, learns these sorts of lessons the same way we do.

Unfortunately, this deep and unconscious way of learning is the driver that can put us onto the treadmill of the cycle of anxiety. Because negative reinforcement evolved before the conscious parts of our brains, it is hard to use our conscious mental faculties to overcome anxiety and the behaviours we devise to defuse or avoid anxiety.

This is how the cycle of anxiety works. We are faced with uncertainty, with a situation or problem that causes

stress. But because we live modern lives, this uncertainty is not going to be a roar in the night. It's going to be giving a presentation in front of your managers at work. It's going to be asking someone you like out on a date. It could also be something like the fear of catching Covid-19 or the political situation in the world.

Our old brains, faced with uncertainty, fill us with the need to do something to make these feelings go away. We could prepare the talk. We could screw up our courage and ask the person on a date. But there are situations that cause uncertainty over which we have no control – there is nothing that we can do.

The feelings grow until we think, maybe I'll call in sick. Someone else can do the talk. Or I decide that person doesn't like me after all, so I won't ask them for a date. In these cases, by doing something we suddenly reduce the anxiety we were under before, but we have done this by avoiding doing what we wanted to do. This brings immediate, short-term relief from anxiety. It makes us feel better.

Unfortunately, this is also stored away in our deep memory, the memory we share with sea slugs, so that next time we face similar feelings of anxiety (sweaty palms, butterflies, shortness of breath) our brains will present to us the same method of

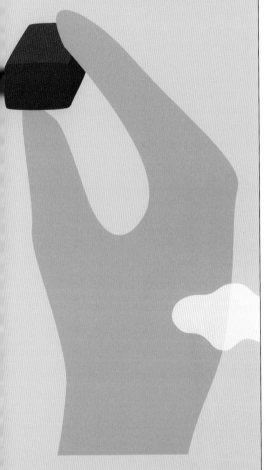

"ANXIETY CAN MAKE PEOPLE WAKE UP IN THE NIGHT FOR NO APPARENT REASON"

SPREADING FEAR

Anxiety is not just personal, it's social too

Anxiety can spread. We are fundamentally social creatures and when we see people around us exhibiting signs of anxiety, then we are probably going to start feeling anxious too. This is called social contagion and it makes perfect sense in our evolutionary past. Seeing another member of the tribe suddenly standing tall, shielding his eyes against the sun while scanning the tall grass would immediately alert us to possible danger. Our survival brain kicks in: *get more information.* Social anxiety even affects high finance: the Volatility Index on Wall Street is colloquially known as 'the fear index'. With anxiety triggers being provided by the people around us or the wider culture, it can be very difficult to counteract the feelings of fear/anxiety by any rational response to what is going on. For instance, in the early months of the Covid-19 pandemic, when no one knew how dangerous the disease was nor how it spread, the uncertainty was real and impossible to relieve by finding out actual information. No one knew the answers. In these circumstances, it is easy for anxiety to spiral out of control, leading to panic. Think of the supermarkets stripped bare of toilet paper, pasta and rice. This was anxiety amplified by social contagion into widespread panic buying. The cycle of anxiety is not just personal, it can spread to take in much of society too.

So, uncertainty and fear over Covid-19 translated into the avoidance behaviour of buying stockpiles of toilet paper. However much toilet paper someone bought, it would not stop them catching the virus, but by doing something it reduced the overwhelming feelings of anxiety.

dealing with these very unpleasant feelings: avoid them. If we do the same thing again the next time we face feelings of anxiety, then the memory becomes deeper and avoidance is set on a track towards becoming a habit.

Of course, there are times when avoidance is the right action. For instance, imagine you are trying to cross a very busy road, and thinking of whether to make a run for it during a break in the traffic. But then you see

means someone else gets a pay rise. Convincing yourself that that person never really liked you makes it harder to believe that anyone would.

However, the worst thing about reducing anxiety through avoidance is that it causes a long-term growth in anxiety. It means that next time an uncertain situation or problem causes feelings of anxiety to spike, it will be harder to deal with these feelings head on because they will have become more intense. That old part of your brain has learned that by increasing the uncomfortable feelings that accompany anxiety, it can force you into a solution more quickly. Remember, the feelings accompanying anxiety exist to make us do something:

that old lizard brain doesn't care what we do, so long as it makes the feelings go away.

Unfortunately, that solution is avoidance. While avoidance brings a short-term reduction in anxiety, each time we avoid uncertainty and its accompanying feelings, we are building a bigger wall of habit.

As the habit of reducing anxiety by avoidance becomes more ingrained, our anxiety levels actually increase each time we are faced with uncertainty. It's that old lizard brain pushing us to do something – anything. As the pattern becomes deeper, it can cause feelings of anxiety to spike even when there is no apparent cause. This can lead to people waking up in the

that there is a pedestrian bridge further up the road, so you cross there. Here, avoidance makes perfect sense.

The cycle of anxiety can be further deepened because so many anxieties we face today are beyond our control. The Covid-19 pandemic was one example and now we are moving into very uncertain political times. These things naturally produce anxious feelings within us, but with situations like this there is nothing we can do. We can't turn back a pandemic or make the world peaceful.

When faced with these uncertainties, the brain might deal with the feelings of anxiety by avoiding them through distraction: watch some cat videos on YouTube, do some gardening, drink. All of these might serve to reduce anxiety but they also serve to groove the avoidance channel more deeply into our repertoire of behaviours.

While avoidance reduces feelings of anxiety in the short term, it carries penalties. Avoiding the talk

"THE WORST THING ABOUT REDUCING ANXIETY THROUGH AVOIDANCE IS THAT IT CAUSES A LONG-TERM GROWTH IN ANXIETY"

middle of the night even when, so far as they know, they have nothing to worry about. But the mere fact they have woken means that surely there must be something to worry about, so the cycle gets deeper. For some people, the act of worrying – and worrying is a behaviour – becomes the avoidance mechanism by which they reduce feelings of anxiety. After all, worrying seems like you're doing something and

that allows the lizard brain to ramp down the feelings of anxiety.

The cycle of anxiety is the result of different parts of our brains each trying to solve problems in the ways they know best. That is what makes it so difficult to break once the cycle has been established. But, thankfully, there are now some excellent therapies and mental tools to help break the cycle of anxiety.

FEAR
EXPLAINED

The biology of being afraid & why this primal emotion is key to your survival

WORDS JACKIE SNOWDEN

Home alone at night, you hear a loud crash. In an instant your heart starts racing, your muscles tense and your breath quickens. You are immediately alert, primed to fight or flee the source of the sound, which turns out to be a pile of books falling off that shelf you've been meaning to fix. But in that moment, your brain and body reacted as if you were in mortal danger.

Fear is one of our strongest and most primal emotions. It's a big bad world out there, and being afraid of certain things protects us from potential danger to make sure we survive. Some evolutionary fears are hard-wired into our brains, but we can also develop new fears throughout our lives. As children we pick up on what makes our parents anxious, and we may also learn to fear certain things after negative experiences. Despite this, most of us are able to ignore our fears when it's clear we aren't in any immediate danger. We can enjoy the view from the top of a skyscraper rather than worry about falling, or turn out the lights safe in the knowledge that a predator won't devour us in the night.

However, people with phobias have an excessive fear response that causes both physical and psychological distress. These extreme fears are divided into three different groups: agoraphobia, social phobia and specific phobias. Agoraphobia is generally referred to as the fear of open spaces, but it applies to the dread of any situation that is difficult to escape from, or where help would not be available if something went wrong. Social phobia is the intense fear of interacting with people or performing, while specific phobias are the fear of a particular situation, activity or thing.

These irrational fears can cause major disruptions to everyday life; somebody with acrophobia – an extreme fear of heights – may experience a panic attack simply trying to walk across a bridge. Depending on the trigger of their phobia, sufferers often go to great lengths to avoid situations that could affect them.

The cause of phobias is not always clear, but many cases are linked to experiencing or witnessing a traumatic event. For example, somebody may develop cynophobia – the fear of dogs – after being bitten. But whether the trigger is rational or irrational, as soon as the brain registers a scary stimulus, it activates the fight-or-flight response, thus preparing the body for action.

"BEING AFRAID OF CERTAIN THINGS PROTECTS US FROM POTENTIAL DANGER"

NATURAL FEARS

Some of our fears have developed as an evolutionary response to danger

DARKNESS

Sight is arguably our most important sense. When we are faced with pitch-darkness we are left vulnerable, unaware of what is around us. At night, our early ancestors were at risk of being attacked by nocturnal predators. A study from 2011 found that even today, the majority of African lion attacks on humans occur after dark, and are more likely when the Moon is below the horizon. Although being hunted while we sleep isn't a risk for most of us, we are instinctively more anxious when unable to see.

HEIGHTS

A fear of heights is necessary to our survival, ensuring we are cautious in situations where we might injure ourselves. To study this, researchers set up a platform surrounded by a transparent material, giving the illusion of a cliff, and put young children on the platform to test their reaction. They found that most infants didn't try to move onto the transparent section, suggesting that they inherently avoided risking a drop. As our ancestors explored the world, this fear ensured they were wary of climbing to dangerous heights.

POISONOUS CREATURES

While we may not be terrified of them from birth, evidence suggests that we are predisposed to detect and recognise spiders and snakes quicker than non-threatening animals. One theory is that our early mammal ancestors, evolving in a world dominated by reptiles, needed to identify and react to snakes to avoid becoming dinner. Another hypothesis is that our ancestors evolving in Africa coexisted with a number of poisonous spider species for millions of years, so being able to spot and avoid them was a vital skill.

FIGHT OR FLIGHT

How your brain and body trigger this evolutionary survival instinct

Usually, sensory information from your body is sent to the thalamus in the brain. The thalamus relays these signals to the cortex and the hippocampus for further processing. This info is forwarded to the amygdala, which triggers an emotional reaction.

When your brain receives signals that indicate some kind of danger, the course of action is slightly different. The process above still occurs, but this higher-level analysis takes precious time. The fraction of a second it takes to fully understand what's happening might be the difference between life and death. To make sure your body is instantly prepared to face a threat, the thalamus also sends the raw sensory information via a shortcut, directly to the amygdala. As soon as the amygdala is alerted, it signals the hypothalamus. This part of the brain activates systems that release around 30 different hormones into the bloodstream. One hormone, adrenaline, causes a variety of physiological reactions all around the body. In the lungs it makes smooth muscle cells relax, expanding the air passages so more oxygen can reach the blood. It also stimulates cardiac cells so the heart beats faster, and makes muscles in the eyes contract to dilate the pupils. The physical changes produced by this sudden flood of hormones make up the fight-or-flight response. This instinct gets you ready to either take a stand and defend yourself, or escape.

More often than not our fight-or-flight response is triggered by a false alarm. It automatically kicks in before the brain evaluates the situation. Once the amygdala concludes that you are not in danger, it signals the thalamus to stop the reaction, returning your body to normal.

FEAR ON THE BRAIN

What happens when the brain goes into survival mode?

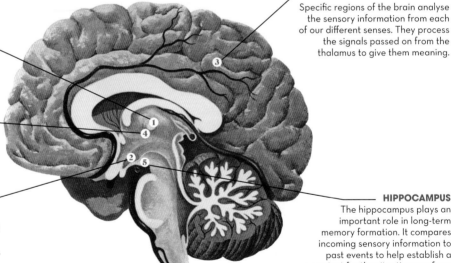

THALAMUS
The thalamus is the first port of call for most sensory signals from the body. It relays this information to the relevant areas of the brain, like a switchboard.

HYPOTHALAMUS
The hypothalamus's primary role is to maintain homeostasis – keeping the body in a stable condition. It also regulates the secretion of hormones and initiates the fight-or-flight response.

AMYGDALA
The amygdala processes our emotional reactions and plays a role in decision-making and the formation of memories. It moderates our responses to events that affect our survival.

SENSORY CORTEX
Specific regions of the brain analyse the sensory information from each of our different senses. They process the signals passed on from the thalamus to give them meaning.

HIPPOCAMPUS
The hippocampus plays an important role in long-term memory formation. It compares incoming sensory information to past events to help establish a context for the situation you face.

1 STIMULUS When a threat is detected, the thalamus sends signals to the amygdala via two different pathways. One route is fast and direct, while the slower path analyses the situation and decides what should happen next.

2 ACT FIRST The first pathway assumes there's danger even if there is none – a safer option than vice versa. It goes to the amygdala, which sends signals to the hypothalamus to initiate the fight-or-flight response.

3 ANALYSIS The same information is sent along the more investigative route. Signals from the thalamus are sent to the sensory cortex, which interprets the data, followed by the hippocampus, to analyse the situation's context.

4 FIGHT OR FLIGHT? The hypothalamus activates both the sympathetic nervous system and the adrenal-cortical system to trigger the fight-or-flight reaction. The impulses and hormones produced prepare the body for action.

5 JUDGEMENT Once the situation has been analysed by the longer pathway, the hippocampus sends signals to the amygdala to either seize the fight-or-flight response if there is no danger, or to maintain it if there is.

ANATOMY OF FEAR

The extreme reactions that occur when your body is put on high alert

WIDE-EYED
The pupils dilate to let in more light, so you can take in more of your surroundings and identify the threat.

GOOSEBUMPS
As your muscles tense up, the small hairs on your skin are forced upright. This evolutionary reflex probably helped our hairier ancestors look bigger and scarier.

RESPIRATION INCREASES
Faster breathing sends more oxygen to your muscles to prepare them for action.

BLOOD RUNS COLD
The vessels in your skin constrict to help divert more blood to your muscles and reduce blood loss from potential injury. This makes you feel cold.

SHAKING MUSCLES
More blood is pumped to the muscles so you can defend yourself or make a quick getaway. This can make your limbs feel tense and twitchy.

"THE TIME IT TAKES TO UNDERSTAND WHAT'S HAPPENING MIGHT BE THE DIFFERENCE BETWEEN LIFE AND DEATH"

HORMONES
The activated sympathetic nervous system and adrenal-cortical system release dozens of hormones into the bloodstream to cause changes in the body.

ENERGY BOOST
Your liver starts breaking down glycogen into glucose, ready to supply the body with instant energy.

COLD SWEAT
Your body anticipates immediate action, so you pre-emptively start to sweat in order to keep cool.

HEART RATE INCREASES
The hormones adrenaline and noradrenaline are released to increase your heart rate, sending more blood to your muscles and brain.

BUTTERFLIES
Blood flow is diverted away from non-essential systems such as digestion. This causes the nervous 'butterflies in your stomach' feeling.

WHY DO WE SCREAM?

Screaming is an innate reflex; it's usually the first thing you do when you're born. Although we might also scream from excitement or pleasure, it is most often a cry of distress. Researchers from New York University conducted an experiment using brain scans to see how our minds react to screams. When we listen to normal speech, what we hear is sent to the auditory cortex for processing so we can make sense of the sounds.

However, the study showed that when we hear a scream, the signals are sent straight to the amygdala to activate the brain's fear response. The team also found that 'rougher' screams – those that change volume more quickly – were the most distressing. The results show that screams are a very effective method of communication in humans. They not only help convey danger, but also help make those who hear them more alert.

ARE FEARS GENETIC?

Your phobias could be passed down through generations in DNA

It was previously assumed that all irrational fears are learned through personal experience or taught to us by others. In cases where a person develops a phobia related to a traumatic event in their past, this is most likely the case.

However, it is now thought that some phobias have a genetic origin. Identical twins are more likely to share the same irrational fears than non-identical twins.

Experiments with mice have shown that fears they develop can be passed down to their children. The mice were conditioned to fear the scent of acetophenone – a sweet-smelling

chemical. Researchers found that the pups, and even the grand-pups, of the mice were startled by the scent too.

One explanation for this could be that parent mice communicate with their pups to teach them what to fear. Studies have found that when mice are scared, they release pheromones that act as an alarm signal. However, in this experiment, the pups proved to be sensitive to the scent from the first time they encountered it. What's more, some pups of conditioned mice were fostered by non-conditioned mice. The non-conditioned foster parents were not afraid of the scent, but the pups were, suggesting the fear's origin was genetic.

It is not clear exactly how the conditioned fear is passed on to future generations of mice, but the current theory is that it is down to something called epigenetic inheritance. The original conditioning process leads to chemical modifications that change gene expression (which genes are switched on or off), without changing the DNA sequence itself. The researchers found that the conditioned mice and their offspring developed more scent receptors in their brains compared to non-conditioned mice. With more of these receptors, they can detect the presence of acetophenone at lower concentrations and so are alerted to it more easily.

INHERITING FEARS

A study with lab mice suggests that fear is a family affair

"IDENTICAL TWINS OFTEN SHARE THE SAME IRRATIONAL FEARS"

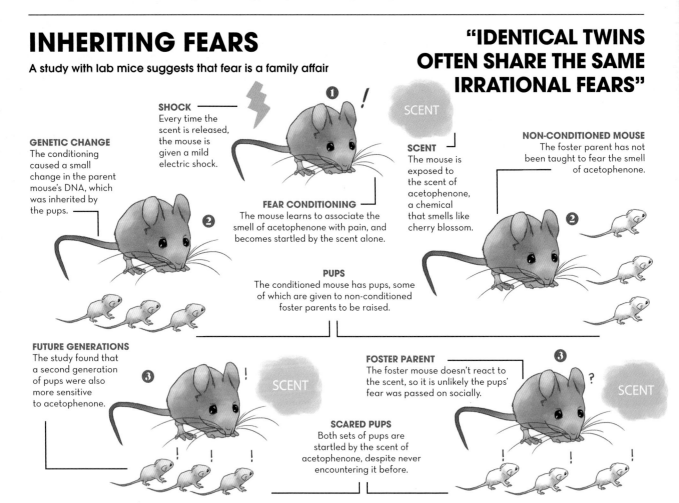

SHOCK
Every time the scent is released, the mouse is given a mild electric shock.

SCENT

GENETIC CHANGE
The conditioning caused a small change in the parent mouse's DNA, which was inherited by the pups.

SCENT
The mouse is exposed to the scent of acetophenone, a chemical that smells like cherry blossom.

NON-CONDITIONED MOUSE
The foster parent has not been taught to fear the smell of acetophenone.

FEAR CONDITIONING
The mouse learns to associate the smell of acetophenone with pain, and becomes startled by the scent alone.

PUPS
The conditioned mouse has pups, some of which are given to non-conditioned foster parents to be raised.

FUTURE GENERATIONS
The study found that a second generation of pups were also more sensitive to acetophenone.

SCENT

FOSTER PARENT
The foster mouse doesn't react to the scent, so it is unlikely the pups' fear was passed on socially.

SCENT

SCARED PUPS
Both sets of pups are startled by the scent of acetophenone, despite never encountering it before.

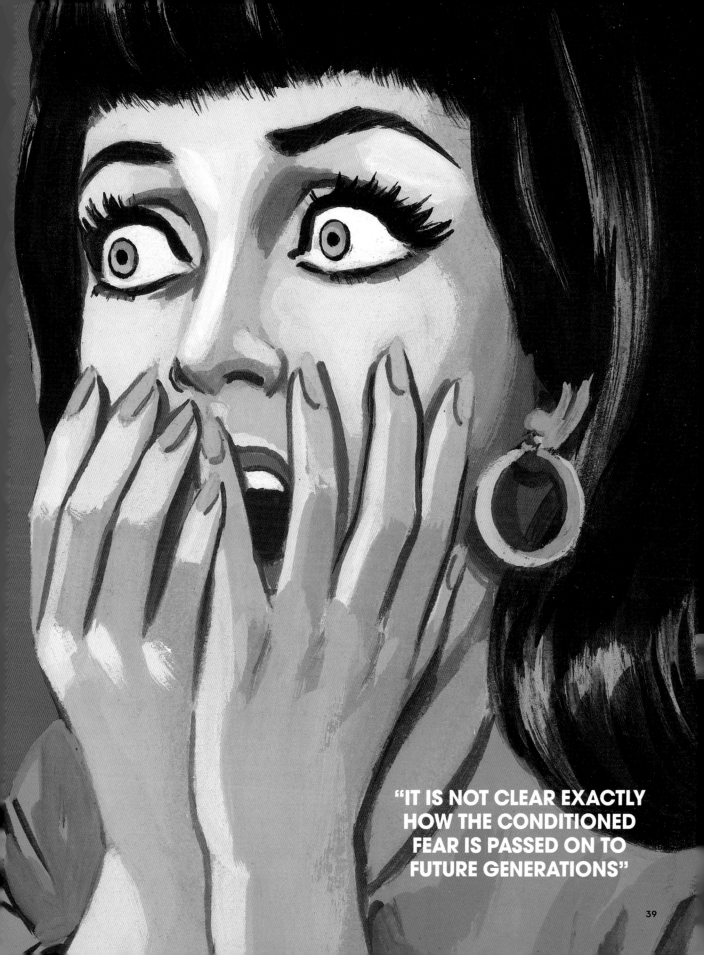

"IT IS NOT CLEAR EXACTLY HOW THE CONDITIONED FEAR IS PASSED ON TO FUTURE GENERATIONS"

LIVING FEARLESSLY

Self-help gurus and motivational posters encourage us to be fearless, but in reality a life without fear would be incredibly dangerous. Studies have shown that when the region of the brain called the amygdala is damaged, people are more likely to take risks. Severe damage can even leave people with no sense of fear whatsoever – which can land them in some pretty scary situations! For the past 25 years, scientists have been studying a patient (known as SM for anonymity) who lacks an amygdala. SM has experienced many traumatic events in her life – she has been held at both knife and gun-point, and was nearly killed during a domestic violence attack – but she did not react with any sense of desperation or urgency, even though her life was in danger. Researchers took SM to an exotic pet store where, despite claiming she hated them, the snakes and spiders captivated her. Scientists noted her curiosity and compulsive desire to touch some of the more dangerous creatures, following repeated warnings from staff. The researchers concluded that SM's inability to detect or react appropriately to threats likely contributed to her disproportionate number of traumatic experiences.

By studying patients like SM, it is hoped that scientists can understand more about fear, and discover new methods of helping people whose lives are plagued by it. For example, treatments that target the amygdala could benefit those who suffer from post-traumatic stress disorder.

SCARED TO DEATH

It's not just a figure of speech – it turns out you really can die of fright. The adrenaline released during the fight-or-flight response can be damaging in large amounts. This stress hormone encourages the heart muscle to contract, but if your body releases too much adrenaline, your heart is unable to relax again. Adrenaline can also interfere with the cells that regulate your heart rhythm, causing it to beat abnormally, which could be lethal. While not directly deadly, prolonged anxiety can have a significant negative impact on your health. The fight-or-flight response suppresses the immune system, leaving you vulnerable to illness. Going into survival mode on a regular basis can lead to digestive disorders as this non-essential system is repressed. Long-term stress can also lead to weight issues by disrupting the metabolism; elevated levels of cortisol can make the body less sensitive to insulin. Muscles that are constantly tense and ready for action can cause headaches, stiffness and neck pain. The list doesn't end there; chronic anxiety has also been linked to cardiovascular problems, asthma and insomnia. Such a broad range of effects can be harmful to both physical and mental wellbeing.

FACING YOUR FEARS

Can you retrain your brain to overcome a phobia?

Some phobia triggers are much easier to avoid than others. For example, people who suffer from a fear of bats (chiroptophobia) are highly unlikely to be plagued by these creatures day in, day out. Someone suffering from a social phobia, however, will struggle to lead a normal life.

There are a variety of different methods used to treat phobias. Among the most popular are talking treatments, such as cognitive behavioural therapy and exposure therapy, which work by retraining the brain to change how it responds to a phobia trigger. The approach is essentially the opposite of fear conditioning – the patient learns to associate their trigger with more rational, positive thoughts.

Another approach being investigated is tricking the brain into treating itself. Mentalist and illusionist Derren Brown conducted an experiment on his programme *Fear And Faith*, in which he gave people with different phobias a new wonder drug called Rumyodin. One subject, usually terrified of heights, was comfortably able to sit on the edge of a tall bridge. Another volunteer with a fear of performing in public was able to go to an audition. It was revealed that Rumyodin (an anagram of 'your mind') didn't exist, and the participants had simply been injected with saline solution and given sugar pills. The incredible results are a demonstration of the placebo effect, a phenomenon in which a fake treatment has a very real result. Scientists are investigating how this effect can be exploited to treat both physical and psychological problems.

© Getty Images, Alamy, Dreamstime, Pixabay

PHOBIA TREATMENTS

EXPOSURE THERAPY

The aim of exposure therapy is to gradually desensitise the patient to the source of their phobia. The patient ranks situations from least to most terrifying. For example, an arachnophobe might place thinking about a spider at the bottom of their list, and having a spider crawl along their arm at the top. The patient works with a psychologist to systematically work their way through the list, using relaxation techniques or other coping mechanisms until they are comfortable with each stage. The patient's brain learns to relate each scary situation to being calm, reducing their anxiety.

COGNITIVE BEHAVIOURAL THERAPY

The aim of cognitive behavioural therapy (CBT) is to change how we think about certain situations. It is thought that irrational anxiety issues are caused by a patient's negative interpretation of events, rather than the events themselves. CBT is a talking therapy that helps patients assess their reactions to situations, replacing the worry cycle with more useful or realistic thoughts.

Patients' brain scans indicate that CBT reduces the overactivity in the amygdala and hippocampus associated with phobias. Studies have also shown that CBT is as effective as medication in the treatment of many anxiety disorders.

VIRTUAL REALITY THERAPY

Exposure therapy isn't a viable option for all phobias, but modern technology offers an alternative. Advancements in virtual reality systems mean that patients can now face their fears through a headset rather than in the real world. This enables patients to face any number of situations relating to their phobia, while knowing they are in no physical danger.

For example, somebody with a phobia of flying can take a course of sessions – in which they board a virtual plane and experience announcements, take-off, turbulence and landing – without having to buy a plane ticket each week.

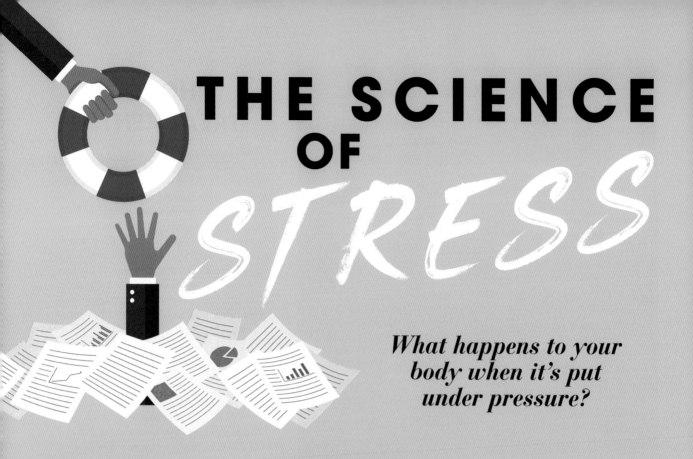

THE SCIENCE OF *STRESS*

What happens to your body when it's put under pressure?

WORDS LAURA MEARS

The man who first defined stress, Hans Selye, once told reporters: "Everyone knows what stress is, but nobody really knows." From a mental health perspective, stress describes the feeling of excessive emotional pressure. It can manifest itself as anxiety, trouble sleeping, altered eating patterns, destructive behaviour, headaches or muscle pain. This is the stress we are all familiar with. But, from a broader biological perspective, stress is the body's response to any kind of disruption, whether it's psychological trauma, extreme temperature, lack of food, or confrontation with a predator.

There's no proper medical definition of stress, but when it comes to biology, it describes any threat to the body's normal balance. In order to cope with that threat, whether it's real or imagined, the body takes steps to protect itself. The bloodstream floods with chemical signals that heighten awareness, increase heart rate, quicken breathing, dull pain, and even induce euphoria. At the same time, non-essential functions like digestion and growth slow right down. When the stress response is activated, surviving becomes the key concern; the future becomes less important.

The brain kick-starts the stress response. The amygdala, which deals with emotion and fear, sends a message to the hypothalamus, setting off a chain of electrical and chemical messages that prepare the body to respond. The first step is to put the nervous system into 'fight or flight' mode. It does this by signalling to the adrenal glands to increase production of adrenaline.

This chemical messenger surges into the bloodstream, triggering a wave of energy release by raiding the body's stores of fats and glycogen. Blood sugar rises and fatty acids are released to fuel the body in its time of need. These molecules are then shuttled to the muscles and brain by the bloodstream. Blood vessels in non-essential areas constrict, heart rate increases and breathing becomes faster, diverting extra resources to the places that need them most. Senses become heightened and the brain is put on alert. This response happens instantly, sometimes even before the conscious brain has processed it.

Depending on the situation – and the individual – the exact pattern of these chemical surges differs. If escape or

"SURVIVING BECOMES THE KEY CONCERN"

THE STRESS RESPONSE

The body has a well-tuned system for dealing with the first signs of stress

1. HYPOTHALAMUS
This part of the brain is responsible for maintaining balance in the body, and it kicks off the stress response.

2. PITUITARY
This pea-sized organ produces many hormones, including the stress messenger adrenocorticotropic hormone.

3. ADRENALS
These glands are found on top of the kidneys, and produce steroids in response to stress.

4. CORTICOTROPIN-RELEASING FACTOR
This chemical messenger carries the stress signal from the hypothalamus to the pituitary.

5. ADRENOCORTICOTROPIC HORMONE
This hormone travels through the bloodstream, carrying the chemical message to the kidneys.

6. CORTISOL
These natural steroids trigger changes across the body, helping it to deal with stress.

7. ACTIVATION
Several areas of the brain feed into the hypothalamus, triggering the stress response.

8. SUPPRESSION
High levels of glucocorticoids in the blood feed back to the brain, switching off the stress response.

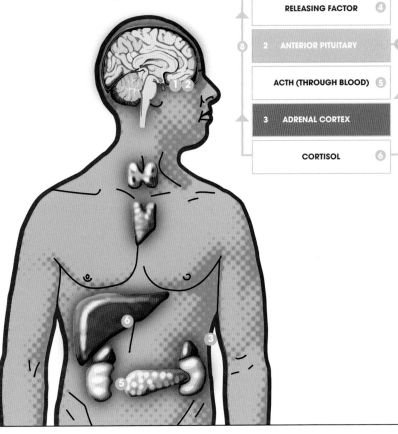

1	HYPOTHALAMUS	7
	RELEASING FACTOR	4
8	2 ANTERIOR PITUITARY	
	ACTH (THROUGH BLOOD)	5
	3 ADRENAL CORTEX	
	CORTISOL	6

STRESS ISN'T JUST HUMAN

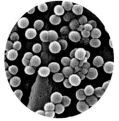

BACTERIA
These microbes cope with changes to their environment by altering the way they use their genes. Molecules called sigma factors change which genes are switched on, and which are turned off.

PLANTS
Water stress can be a real problem for plants, so they respond by conserving moisture. This includes producing rapid chemical signals that close the pores in their leaves.

FISH
Fish have a similar stress response to other vertebrates, with a cycle of chemical signals that starts in the brain, preparing the body to release energy and shut down unnecessary activity.

BIRDS
Like us, birds make corticosteroids in response to stress. The amount goes up in birds that breed in higher places, which helps them to cope with the risks associated with nesting at high altitudes.

MICE
These rodents are often used as a model for human biology, but recent research showed that they are stressed by male scientists. The effect seems to be related to their smell, and it may skew the results of tests.

THE EFFECTS OF STRESS

Too much stress can have a negative effect on different parts of the body

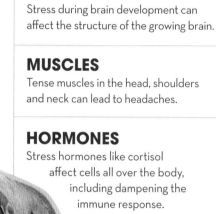

The pituitary gland is packed with hormone-producing endocrine cells

BREATHING

An increased breathing rate can result in panic attacks and hyperventilation.

HEART RATE

Raised heart rate and blood pressure can cause gradual damage to the cardiovascular system.

RESPIRATION INCREASES

Faster breathing sends more oxygen to your muscles to prepare them for action.

NERVES

Stress during brain development can affect the structure of the growing brain.

MUSCLES

Tense muscles in the head, shoulders and neck can lead to headaches.

HORMONES

Stress hormones like cortisol affect cells all over the body, including dampening the immune response.

DIGESTION

Changes in blood flow to the digestive system and different eating patterns can affect bowel function.

REPRODUCTION

Fertility and libido can be affected by chronic stress in both men and women.

"IT TURNS OUT THAT IF WE BELIEVE THAT STRESS IS BAD, IT IS MORE LIKELY TO DO US HARM"

confrontation is not an option, another response, known as 'aversive vigilance' might replace 'fight or flight'. Under these circumstances, movement stops, and blood is diverted away from the skin and extremities to the organs in the core.

Rather than revving the body up for physical activity, this response helps to minimise bleeding in case of injury.

Though most stresses we experience now don't carry a risk of physical harm, this would have been useful in our evolutionary past. Which response is chosen varies on circumstances, but individuals are more likely to favour one or the other, and it's thought that these patterns are set early in life.

At the same time, a slower but more persistent stress response is

also activated. The hypothalamus pumps out a molecule called corticotropin-releasing factor (CRF). This is the trigger for the biological response that puts the body into survival mode. From the hypothalamus, CRF hops a short distance through the bloodstream to the pituitary gland, where it triggers the release of a second, longer-range chemical message. Known as adrenocorticotropic hormone (ACTH),

EUSTRESS VS DISTRESS

How can stress levels affect our ability to work?

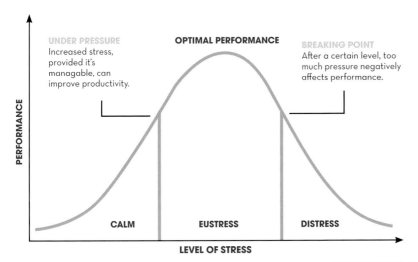

UNDER PRESSURE
Increased stress, provided it's managable, can improve productivity.

OPTIMAL PERFORMANCE

BREAKING POINT
After a certain level, too much pressure negatively affects performance.

PERFORMANCE

CALM   EUSTRESS   DISTRESS

LEVEL OF STRESS

STRESS-RELATED DAMAGE

Long-term, or chronic, stress can be bad for our health, but it's challenging to pin down exactly why. Is it to do with poor lifestyle choices made under pressure, or is there something happening inside the body as a result of a prolonged stress response?
In 2004, a research team from the US published a paper in the journal *PNAS* that investigated what happens to our cells under stress. They looked at the genetic code, homing in on the protective caps that cover the ends of each chromosome. Known as telomeres, these structures shorten as cells get older. An enzyme called telomerase can replenish telomeres, but stress diminishes the supply of this regenerative enzyme. The team studied a group of 58 women, and they found that the longer the women had been stressed, and the more stressed they felt, the more likely they were to have shortened telomeres – a sign that their bodies were feeling the strain. Exactly why this happens is not currently known.

GOOD STRESS?

In 1936, endocrinologist Hans Selye wrote a letter to the scientific journal *Nature*, describing the "general alarm reaction of the organism." He was one of the first people to identify and investigate biological stress. He continued his investigations, and after nearly 40 years of research, Selye came to the conclusion that stress wasn't all bad.
People had known for a long time that there's a link between 'stress' and productivity. In 1908, two researchers, Yerkes and Dodson, showed that there's a sweet-spot, where there's just enough pressure to encourage productivity, but not so much that it becomes too much for the person to handle.
Selye was interested in the idea that the feeling of stress isn't so much about what happens to the body, but about how each individual reacts to the changes.
In the 1970s, he introduced two new words, 'eustress' and 'distress', to describe what he saw. Eustress was beneficial stress, and distress was bad.

this molecule travels around the body in the bloodstream, reaching the kidneys, where it triggers the next step in the stress response process.

On top of each kidney is a hormone factory known as an adrenal gland, and within each is a compartment known as the adrenal cortex. The cells

here produce glucocorticoids, the body's natural steroids. And it's these steroids that help the rest of the body to deal with stress. Cortisol interferes with insulin, helping to keep blood sugar levels up. It helps to balance the body's pH; it dampens the immune response; and it even affects the formation of memories.

Short-term stress is quickly corrected by the body, and, to prevent the cycle continuing forever, the cortisol also acts as an off switch. It feeds back to the brain, letting it know that the stress response has been fully activated, and helps to switch off the production of CRF and ACTH. But sometimes, stress can develop into a long-term, chronic problem.

Humans are unique among animals (as far as we know) in that we think abstractly about the world and ourselves. Our huge brains are a gift, but can also lead to long-term stress as we worry over problems that just wouldn't occur to other animals, like work and money.

While the stress response has been honed by evolution to boost the chances of survival during short periods of increased environmental pressure, in the long term it can cause damage. Ultimately, it can lead to illness if left unchecked.

Exposure to stress during childhood, be it war, neglect or even divorce, can make people more likely to experience mental health problems as adults. During this period, the brain is still developing, and chronic stress can cause structural changes that affect the way that it functions. As adults, chronic stress puts strain on the heart and blood vessels, contributing to

BLOCKING STRESS MOLECULES

The hypothalamus is the part of the brain responsible for kicking off the stress response, and it does this by producing corticotropin-releasing factor (CRF). This hormone travels to the nearby pituitary gland, where it tells the cells to begin pumping out adrenocorticotropic hormone (ACTH), which in turn tells the kidneys to make the stress steroid cortisol. One of the critical molecules in this pathway is known as CRF1: corticotropin-releasing factor receptor 1. It is the molecule that detects the CRF, and in 2013, scientists managed to work out its shape.

CRF1 sits on the surface of cells in the pituitary, and other structures in the body, and waits for CRF to arrive. When it does, the hormone sticks to the receptor and triggers molecular pathways that contribute to the stress response. Understanding its shape could help drug developers to design treatments that interfere with this interaction, stopping the hormone from slotting into its hole in the receptor, dampening the stress.

This is corticotropin-releasing hormone. It binds to CRF1 to trigger part of the stress response

STRUCTURE
CRH is comprised of 41 amino acids.

DISEASE
Increased CRH production is associated with Alzheimer's.

© Getty Images

MONITORING STRESS

The tech that can tell if you're having a tough time

There are several electronic gadgets that claim to be able to track your stress levels by tapping in to your heart rate, breathing, skin conductance and blood oxygen. The idea is to help you to identify, and avoid, your stress triggers. However, although some of the science behind the measurements they take is sound, it's not always easy to decipher what they mean. For example, the time between heartbeats varies less when you are stressed, but also when you are excited. A device that picks up on these changes won't be able to tell you which mood you are in unless it knows what else is happening around you.

cardiovascular disease, heart attacks and strokes, and it can also damage the immune system.

During an acute stress response, immune cells are mobilised in case they need to fend off infection, but the stress steroid cortisol affects their function in the long term. In fact, drugs based on cortisol are used to dampen down the immune system in patients in need of immunosuppression.

Long-term stress can be a real problem. Not only does the response itself put pressure on the body, but coping mechanisms, including drinking and smoking, can all damage our insides. However, it's not just about the physical effects. 'Stress' is a loaded word, and recent research has been looking at how our perceptions of stress affect its impact on the body. It turns out that if we believe stress is bad, it is more likely to do us harm.

Studies in the US have shown that people who are stressed have an increased risk of dying. But – and this is critical – only if they believed that

stress itself could cause them harm. In fact, people who were stressed but didn't believe it was bad for them had a lower risk of dying than those who were barely stressed at all.

The negative connotations of the word 'stress' bothered Hans Selye, who had first pointed out the stress response in the 1930s. Part of the trouble is that stress isn't just used to describe the body's response to challenging situations. In physics, strain is the change in shape or size of an object as a result of an external force, and stress is the internal force associated with it. The use of the same word links the two in people's minds.

Astonishingly, changing the way you think about stress seems to be able to change the effect it has on you. Seeing sweaty palms, increased heart rate and rapid breathing as signs that your body is trying to help you alters your internal response. Heart rate still increases, but blood vessels can stay relaxed, which is much better

"OUR HUGE BRAINS ARE A GIFT, BUT CAN LEAD TO LONG-TERM STRESS"

for the cardiovascular system. What's more, there's another component to the stress response that is often overlooked: oxytocin.

Popularly known as the 'cuddle hormone', oxytocin helps mothers to bond to their babies, and it's released by the brain when we are hugged. It is also produced during stress, helping us to seek social support. Oxytocin also helps by dilating blood vessels, lowering blood pressure and even helping to repair the heart.

While stress can feel unpleasant, it is there to help us deal with life's challenges. Believing in your body, and seeking support when things become too much, can help keep it under control.

ANXIETY IN CHILDREN

Up to one in five children will experience anxiety during their childhood. As parents it's difficult to know when – or even if – we should seek professional support. Consultant Paediatrician Dr Sinead Doyle answers commonly asked questions to put your mind at rest

WORDS BEN GRAFTON

DR SINEAD DOYLE
CONSULTANT COMMUNITY PAEDIATRICIAN

Dr Sinead Doyle is a Consultant Community Paediatrician, specialising in the care of children with physical, emotional and learning difficulties. During her career she has worked with children for whom anxiety has been a key feature of their condition.

How do I know if my child is suffering from anxiety?

Many parents might ask themselves this question and it's not something that gets talked about enough. I always say to parents it's important to trust your parental instinct. If you think something is not right with your child, or they appear to be more worried than they should be, it's really important to seek advice and support.

In some cases, children can be labelled as 'difficult' or 'attention seeking', when in fact they might be displaying signs that they are struggling with their mental and emotional health. Children's behaviour is often a form of communication, and I think it's important that in some cases we consider what they're trying to tell us.

It can of course be entirely normal for children and young people to have worries. However, if these are starting to significantly impact on their daily life at home or at school, you might want to consider seeking further support.

What are some signs of anxiety in school children?

As with adults, anxiety can often manifest in children and young people in the form of physical symptoms. These include dizziness, pain (such as head and tummy aches), nausea or change in appetite, and difficulty sleeping. Older children might describe more typical symptoms, such as chest tightness or difficulty catching their breath. In some cases, medical advice is sought for these physical symptoms before the possibility of underlying anxiety is considered. It is therefore always important to consider whether a physical symptom in a child or young person might be their way of expressing their emotional needs. For other children, however, anxiety might be demonstrated in their behaviour. They might be expressing frequent worry or seeking constant reassurance. They might be demonstrating avoidant behaviours, such as refusing to go to school, or comforting behaviours, such as comfort eating. For many children of school age,

"CHILDREN CAN BE LABELLED AS 'DIFFICULT' OR 'ATTENTION SEEKING', WHEN IN FACT THEY MIGHT BE DISPLAYING SIGNS THAT THEY ARE STRUGGLING WITH THEIR MENTAL AND EMOTIONAL HEALTH"

they may be able to talk to you about their worries directly. However, for children with speech or communication difficulties, for example, different strategies may be needed to help them communicate their feelings.

Do babies and toddlers experience anxiety, too?

For babies and toddlers, anxiety around everyday life is less common because the world in which they live is much smaller, and their cognitive and emotional understanding of the world is a lot less developed. They won't worry about bullying or not having their homework done on time, for example.

As infants, we are wholly dependent on our parents, and so our main concerns are around having our physical and emotional needs met. We know that having a secure attachment as an infant to our main caregiver is important for our future mental and emotional health. Where consistent care and nurture isn't provided, this can lead to anxiety, as well as other developmental difficulties, in later childhood.

As toddlers, we start to widen our social network – we develop relationships with other children, and attend group settings, such as playgroups and nursery. For some children there can be some anxiety associated with this transition, which some might term 'separation anxiety'.

What exactly is separation anxiety?

The emotional attachment between children and their parents is a natural biological imperative which ensures that as children we are kept safe and our needs are met. However, as we grow and begin to explore the world around us, it is important for our

development that we can feel able to detach from our parents. This might be more difficult for some children, and anxiety might develop during periods of transition into nursery or school, for example. Children might struggle to settle without their parents being present in the room, or may look to them frequently for a sense of reassurance and security.

Separation anxiety is common and there are strategies which can help your child to overcome it. In some cases comfort objects, or a gradual introduction into a new environment can be useful. It can be difficult emotionally for parents, too, and so it is important to seek support if you're worried. Depending on the age of your child, you could consider speaking to your child's health visitor – these are specialist nurses who are trained in the care and development of young children. Or if applicable, you could speak to staff at your child's nursery or school.

What sort of anxiety disorders do children commonly experience?

This book covers some of the main anxiety disorders, all of which can present in childhood and adolescence. For some children, their symptoms will be fairly clear cut, allowing a specific diagnosis (such as 'obsessive compulsive disorder') to be made by an appropriately trained professional. Having a specific diagnosis in some cases can be useful in deciding the best way forward in terms of treatment and support. For some children, more than one diagnosis might be given ('anxiety and OCD', for example) as it is well recognised that many of these disorders coexist or overlap.

For many children, however, any symptoms of anxiety may be mild, fluctuant, or even appropriate to the situation. We can all appreciate that exam periods, for example, or even world events, such as the recent Covid-19 pandemic, are inevitably going to impact on mental health. As professionals, when we discuss mental health with children or young people, we try to think about what we call their 'lived experience'. What is their family life like? Where do they go to school? We try to build a picture of the child's life, and think about some of the things that are going well for them, as well as the areas that they feel need more support. Approaching children individually, focusing on their specific symptoms, needs and goals, allows their management to be tailored to them.

My child has a phobia. Is that normal?

Certain fears or anxieties

as children are normal, as we try to process and make sense of the world around us. We can all recall as children the fear of 'what's under the bed' or 'what's in the cupboard'. Fear of the dark, for example, is common, and night lights or comfort toys at bedtime often help children to settle and sleep well.

Some perceived irrational fears might persist into later childhood and

> "CERTAIN FEARS OR ANXIETIES AS CHILDREN ARE NORMAL, AS WE TRY TO MAKE SENSE OF THE WORLD"

even adulthood, however, we only start to worry if these fears begin to have a significant impact on a child or young person's daily life. For example, if the fear means that they're not able to attend school or take part in play or leisure activities, then professional support may be needed. There are 'desensitisation' strategies, among others, which can help a child to overcome or adapt to their phobia.

Could my child's anxiety be linked to something more serious?

For many children, symptoms of anxiety will fall into what is perceived as the 'acceptable' or 'normal' range, although this might be different for different people. Children also cope differently, and some children are very good at finding strategies to support themselves, whether that's through peer relationships or through hobbies. Many children and young people cope with a certain degree of anxiety without the need for professional support.

In some cases, however, there may be concerns that anxiety is significantly impacting a child's mental or physical health. If you are concerned that your child's anxiety is impacting on their physical health - for example, if their sleep or their growth is being affected - you should seek support.

You should also seek support if you feel their mental and emotional health, or their learning, is being

impacted. For example, if they are increasingly withdrawn, struggling with friendships or relationships, or if they are not able to attend school. For some children, consideration may be given to the possibility of an underlying neurodevelopmental disorder, such as autistic spectrum disorder or attention deficit and hyperactivity disorder (ADHD), depending on their specific needs and difficulties.

"MANY YOUNG PEOPLE COPE WITH A CERTAIN DEGREE OF ANXIETY WITHOUT EXPERT INTERVENTION"

What are some good sources of information if I am worried about anxiety in my child?

If you are concerned, there are a number of easily accessible avenues of support. You can discuss any difficulties with your GP in the first instance. They should be able to sign-post you to the appropriate service or support.

For preschool-aged children, they should have an allocated health visitor who will be trained and experienced in supporting children with issues including sleep difficulties, toileting, eating, and emotional and behavioural support.

Every area has what's termed the 'Local Offer' – this is the range of services available in your area, and is usually accessible via your local council website. This includes mental health support accessible through the NHS, local charities for children and young people, as well as other avenues of support such as parent support groups. For most of these services, you will be able to self-refer without going through your GP.

For children who are school age there is the school nursing service. You can speak to your child's school or your GP about how to access this. School nurses are trained in supporting emotional and behavioural health, including support with anxiety. Schools themselves may also be able to offer advice and support. Many have access to counselling services, and other forms of therapy, such as 'play therapy' or 'art therapy'. They are also able to link in with community support teams.

Finally, there are larger, nationally run charities such as Mind (**mind.org.uk**), Young Minds (**youngminds.org.uk**) and Childline (**childline.org.uk**), which all have excellent resources for young people and families seeking support with mental and emotional health.

How can I help my children in their struggles with anxiety?

The first thing I would suggest is to simply try and have a dialogue with your child. It's not always easy, but reassuring your child that they can approach you and talk to you about their worries is a great first step. If you are able to identify specific triggers for your child's anxiety, it is then easier to address them as a family, with support from other professionals as needed. Don't be afraid to speak to the professionals who support your child, including medical professionals, teachers, social care workers and other support workers.

Simple strategies can be useful – there are some excellent ones listed on the Young Minds website. These might include, for example, providing your child with a 'worry book', where they can write down their worries before they go to bed. For other children, it might be the use of picture cards or the 'traffic light system' to describe how they are feeling.

For children, 'mental health hygiene' is no less important than in adults. By this we mean, taking time to do things which are positive for our mental and emotional wellbeing. This might include making time to exercise, time to see friends and play, time for hobbies, eating healthily and regularly, and making sure we get a good night's sleep. With the advent of social media, there are new wider social pressures on young people,

and it is therefore important to manage your child's screen time, and consider the importance of 'online safety' and what they are being exposed to through social media.

How has addressing anxiety in children changed in recent years?
One of the key things is that people are talking about mental health in a more open way. I think children and young people are becoming more literate in the language of mental and emotional health. The stigma that used to surround mental health difficulties is starting to dissipate, which is such a positive thing. The media has played a role in this, as has the voice of charities through their advocacy and campaigns. I talked earlier about the negative impacts of social media, however, in some cases social media can be a positive force, and I think it too has helped to spread positive messages about the importance of mental health, particularly during the Covid-19 pandemic.

Everyone who cares for or works with children in some capacity now plays a role in ensuring they are supported with their mental and emotional health.

That's not to say that there isn't a role for technology, and I think as medical professionals, we are very open to embracing new ways of working, with the goal of improving patient care and experience.

Are children ever prescribed medication for anxiety?

It is not common to prescribe anxiety medication for children, and these would only be prescribed by specialists working in the area of children's mental health. For many children, support strategies, counselling, and other therapies are very effective at offering support. A small minority of children may receive medication treatment, usually where there is a specific underlying diagnosis and with specialist support. This is more likely in older school-age children and adolescents, and is often used in conjunction with therapies.

How can I feel less alone in dealing with my child's anxiety?

I think the key message is you're not alone, even though at times it might feel like it. There is a lot of support out there, particularly since the Covid-19 pandemic, not only from professionals, but also from other parents through parent support groups. Speaking to another parent who has been in a similar situation can be very useful. Don't be afraid to ask for help – if in doubt, speak to someone you feel you have a good understanding with, such as your child's teacher, or another keyworker or mentor. If they don't have the answers, they should be able to direct you to someone who does.

It's also important that parents remember to look after their own wellbeing. Caring for a child with anxiety and other emotional health needs can be a worrying and stressful time, and I try to remind parents that to do the best for their children, they also have to do the best for themselves.

Can technology help my child with their anxiety?

Yes. Many adolescents might not want to speak to their parents or their GP. They might want more non-traditional ways of getting support. Many local services supporting young people's mental health now offer other ways of making contact, such as through text message or online chat. There are also websites and online resources for young people, as well as phone lines where young people can receive direct support.

Technology is also changing the way that we provide healthcare services. Since the Covid-19 pandemic, we carry out increasing numbers of consultations online through 'video' consultations. This can be useful for children who may feel more comfortable speaking to a professional from home rather than in a clinical setting.

Do you think technology will ever replace human contact?

I'm not sure if technological advances, such as artificial intelligence, can replace the human experience or human 'touch', particularly when it comes to mental and emotional health. When someone is struggling, one thing they need is to feel listened to and heard, and I'm not sure if that can be achieved through a computer.

55

GROUNDING TECHNIQUES
TO STOP ANXIETY

Things to do to stop your mind spinning out of control

WORDS EDOARDO ALBERT

Chronic anxiety is bad enough but sometimes these thoughts and feelings can spiral out of control, leading to a full-on panic attack. Panic attacks are deeply scary. While gripped by one, it can feel as if you are about to die. So it is important to find techniques and exercises that can calm us down from a panic attack.

Panic attacks happen when the feedback loop of the cycle of anxiety runs wild. The deep parts of our brain, in particular the amygdala, which produces fear, pick up on a trigger that has become attached to something that makes us anxious. It could be as simple as a passing thought. Where anxiety has become chronic, embedding itself in our thoughts and behaviours, it could simply be the spike in hormones caused by eating a sugary snack is enough to cause our amygdala to kick in. The amygdala evolved to deal with immediate danger. When a trigger activates it, the amygdala immediately floods our bodies with hormones so that we are ready to fight or flee. Our hearts beat faster, muscles tense, breath speeds up. But with no perceptible threat, our body, which is now poised for immediate danger, does not know what to do. With no information telling it whether to fight or run away, the amygdala continues pumping us with action-stations hormones until a full-blown panic attack ensues.

To stop this, we need to signal to the body and the brain that it's all right: there's no danger. Consciously telling ourselves to calm down does not work because the amygdala lies beneath our conscious minds. To approach it, we have to go through the body – which is where these grounding techniques come in.

There are many different techniques but they all work towards bringing us out of a panicked mental state and into the immediate present - where there is no danger. Different techniques work for different people so it might be necessary to try a few before you find something that works best for you. It is best to practise them before a panic attack so that you know the exercise: the middle of a panic attack is not the time to be trying to remember what to do next.

ANXIETY APPS

There are apps for everything nowadays

CALM
£39.99 annually
Calm is primarily a meditation app, guiding the user through a wide range of meditations. It also plays calming sounds and features a growing set of stories designed for restfulness. It's had ten million downloads and consistently receives positive reviews from its users.

MINDSHIFT
Free
Mindshift is a cognitive behavioural therapy (CBT) based app that uses established methods of CBT to help overcome anxiety. It's particularly useful to use after completing a CBT course with a therapist as it helps remind the user to continue with the strategies learned.

FINCH
Free/in-app purchases for more features
Finch works by having the app's titular bird stand in for you. So you take care of the bird by taking care of yourself. Unlike other apps, it has no pressure-based reinforcements, which makes it suitable for anyone who finds more goal-based apps too difficult or stressful.

REFLECTLY
£57.99/year
Reflectly works well with journaling and mood tracking, providing different ways to record your emotions and situation. The app asks you questions to prompt more insight and engagement with your feelings, as well as providing motivations and reminders to keep going.

HEADSPACE
£9.99/month or £49.99/year
Headspace is a meditation and mindfulness app designed by former Buddhist monk, Andy Puddicombe. The app has guided meditation exercises as well as a large number of mindfulness scenarios, some expressly designed to help users cope with anxiety and stress.

5-4-3-2-1 TECHNIQUE

Employing the five senses to return to the present

During a panic attack, or when we can feel anxiety ramping up, the body and brain are locked into a feedback loop. Feelings of anxiety make the deep brain think it is in danger, which leads to it pumping out emergency hormones while getting the body ready to fight or flee. These elevated physical levels feed the physical sensations that accompany anxiety, making us more anxious, which leads to the deep brain pumping out even more emergency hormones. But all of this is going on inside us. There is no danger. Even if the anxiety trigger is something like a forthcoming event, the event is not yet: there is no need to panic. However, the deep part of the brain does not know this.

Future fear has translated into a panic attack in the present. If we can pull our focus back to the present, where in fact there is nothing dangerous, then the body can respond in turn. The 5-4-3-2-1 technique is a way of dissolving future fears into the immediate reality of our surroundings. To begin, as an immediate calming technique,

slow the breath. Breathe in for a count of four and then out for a count of four. Repeat.

Keep this breathing pattern throughout the exercise but the next time you breathe out, look around your surroundings and say, out loud, the names of five things you can see. They could be in the room with you – the chair, a bookcase – or outside, visible through a window – a tree, the sky, someone passing by. Then, again speaking out loud, say the names of four things you can hear. They can be things loud or quiet, near or far. The point is to focus the attention in your ears at this point. The third step is to say three things you can feel. This could be the chair under your bottom to the weight of clothes on your shoulder to the touch of a breeze on the cheek. We are working our way through the five senses, employing each sense in turn to turn our attention from the thoughts and feelings inside our mind to the exterior world immediately around us – a world which is calm and safe. By going through the senses in turn, we

are conveying a message to our amygdala, which listens to the senses much more closely than it listens to our conscious thoughts, that everything is all right.

The fourth step is to name two things we can smell. For those of us who don't have particularly sensitive senses of smell it might work to carry around something that has a distinctive odour that we can focus on when we need to employ the 5-4-3-2-1 technique. A bottle of perfume or a stick of chewing gum. The chewing gum will come in useful for the final step: taste. It does not matter what you use to engage the sense of taste but something pleasant will help to wind the exercise down calmly.

The 5-4-3-2-1 technique is a focused sensory technique to shift our focus away from the storm of internal thoughts and feelings of a panic attack to the world outside ourselves. The technique conveys the message to our autonomic nervous system through all five senses that everything really is all right and it can switch off its emergency response.

BREATHE

When panic takes over, controlling our breath is one of the best ways of getting back in control

Panic attacks produce hyperventilation. Hyperventilation floods our muscles with oxygen, making it ready to fight or to run away. But in a panic attack, there is nothing to run away from. Our deep brain is preparing us for a situation from our deep past when what we are actually facing is the fear of giving a presentation or nerves before an exam. The situations that produce anxiety in the modern world are rarely resolved by fighting or running away.

One way to tell our amygdala that there really is nothing to worry about is to control the breath. By controlling our breathing we can nudge the brain and nervous system out of the flight/fight response. To do so, we need to change the breath pattern into an inbreath to a slow count of four and an outbreath to a slow count of four, preferably through the nose. It's important that the count is the same length for both. At the start, when panic breathing has kicked in, it might be difficult to breathe through the nose but as soon as it is possible, we should switch to nose breathing. The difficulty with this technique is holding on to the slow, even breath count no matter what thoughts and feelings are assailing us, because it takes a little while for the message of slow, steady breathing to get through to the deep brain. But holding to slow, even breathing will send a message through the body to the deep brain: there is no emergency, switch off the danger hormones.

Note that some magazine articles advocate breathing out for twice as long as the inbreath, so an inbreath to the count of four and an outbreath to the count of eight. This rarely works as that breathing pattern works to put our system into its rest/digest state. Trying to switch immediately from the fight/flight response to rest/digest is simply too big a step – the body might panic even further at having these contradictory signals being sent to it. Using calm, slow breathing, with an even breath count puts us into a neutral physiological state, ready to respond to external stimuli. This allows the deep brain to reset itself and us to come out of the panic attack. The best way to prepare for dealing with a panic attack is to practise the long, 4/4 breath pattern beforehand, so that it has become grooved by repetition.

> "BY CONTROLLING OUR BREATHING WE CAN NUDGE THE BRAIN AND NERVOUS SYSTEM OUT OF THE FLIGHT/ FIGHT RESPONSE"

INHALE 4 SECS, HOLD 4 SECS

EXHALE 4 SECS, HOLD 4 SECS

REPEAT X 5

PROGRESSIVE MUSCLE RELAXATION

Learning how to relax the muscles of the body

When we are anxious, our muscles tense. They do this because the deep brain is preparing the body for action, getting it ready to fight or run. However, people suffering from generalised anxiety disorder (GAD), the most common form of anxiety disorder, who live in a constant state of chronic anxiety, can have their muscles in a habitual, permanent state of tension. Progressive muscle relaxation is a way to systematically work through the muscle groups of the body, learning the difference between tension and relaxation, and discovering how to successively relax the muscles in one's body.

This is one technique that must be thoroughly practised, ideally twice a day at first. It takes about 15 minutes and you will need a room where you won't be disturbed. Start by lying on the ground or sitting comfortably in a chair. Take five long, slow even breaths.

Progressive muscle relaxation works by targeting muscle groups in turn. You first tense the muscle group as much as possible, for instance by squeezing your hand into the tightest fist you can manage. After five seconds, breathe out and relax those muscles. Concentrate on how the muscles feel when relaxed as opposed to when they are tense. You are learning what a relaxed muscle feels like.

People usually find it most effective working from feet to head or head to feet. We will look at feet to head but the sequence can be reversed. Some people find it helpful to have a recording to take them through the different muscle groups until they have learned them all.

Start by tensing one foot, curling the toes downwards. Hold, then relax, concentrating on the feel of a relaxed muscle. Then tighten the calf of the same leg by curling the toes upwards. Finish the leg by tensing the thigh muscles. Repeat on the other leg.

Clench one hand, then relax. Tense the whole arm by drawing your clenched fist to your shoulder. Repeat with the other arm.

Moving on to the trunk, start by tightening and then releasing the buttocks. Next, tense and relax your stomach. Tense the chest by taking and holding a really big breath, then breathe out.

To tense the neck and shoulders, hunch your shoulders towards your ears and then relax. Open the mouth as wide as it will go and then relax. Squish your eyes as tight shut as possible and then open them. Finally, tense your forehead by raising your eyebrows as high as you can, and then relax.

Once the exercise is familiar and you know what a relaxed muscle

"THE END RESULT SHOULD BE A RELAXED BODY AND MIND"

feels like, you might want to switch to tensing and releasing sections of the body together: both legs, torso, arms and neck, head. Finally, it may become possible to skip tensing completely and simply work through the body, relaxing each muscle group in turn.

The end result should be a relaxed body. As our brains work in partnership with our bodies, this will tell the brain that it can relax too.

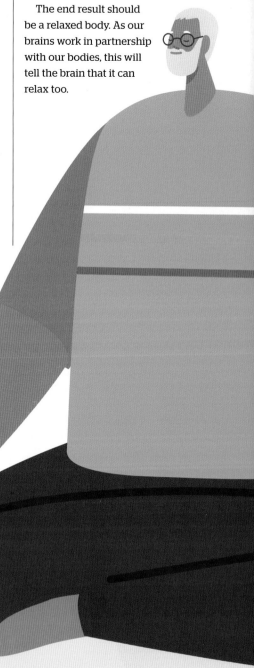

3-3-3 RULE

Pulling back from panic by the threes

The 3-3-3 rule is similar to the 5-4-3-2-1 technique. It employs our two key senses, sight and hearing, and then finishes with our most fundamental sense, the kinaesthetic: our ability to sense the position and movements of our body. The aim is the same: to move the focus from the feedback doom loop of anxiety to the external environment and then parts of our own body. Doing so sends definite signals to the brain that there is no emergency and it can stop releasing emergency hormones into the body. As with all these grounding techniques, the 3-3-3 rule will work better if you practise it in less stressful situations before having to employ it during a full-blown panic attack. An excellent way to groove it into our mental space is to employ the 3-3-3 rule to deal with mild

and moderate anxiety symptoms. Assuming the technique works in these cases will help you feel more confident that it will work in extremis. You will also have experience using the technique when things are more difficult.

To do the 3-3-3 rule, first look around your surroundings and say out loud the names of three things you can see. These must be physical things that you are looking at. As you name each object, really look at it, as if you are seeing it for the first time. Notice all the details of the object that one normally skates past. Even the grain in the paint on a wall can provide something to look at. Look at these objects as a painter would look at them when trying to capture them on canvas.

Then listen. Listen and say out loud what you are hearing.

Name these three sounds, again paying attention to the subtleties of what you are hearing. Is the noise of a jet plane approaching you or getting further away? Is the sound of the kettle constant or does it vary? What pitch is the ring of the phone?

Having employed two external senses, we then move to our internal physical sense of where our body is in space and how it is moving. Name three parts of your body in turn and move them, one after the other. Say, "Index finger," and tap it against the table. Touch your lips with your tongue. Rotate your right foot by moving the ankle. As with the first two, concentrate as you move so that you feel the motions as you are making them, feeling the working of the muscles in your body.

As with all the exercises, combining this technique with slow, even breathing, in for the count of four and out for the count of four, will give your body further cues to shut down its panic response.

"THE 3-3-3 RULE WILL WORK BETTER IF YOU PRACTISE IT IN LESS STRESSFUL SITUATIONS BEFORE HAVING TO EMPLOY IT DURING A PANIC ATTACK"

MOOD TRACKING

Discover the hidden cues and nuances of your feelings

One of the key steps in freeing ourselves from the doom loop of anxiety is finding out what triggers anxious feelings. A therapist will often ask a client to keep a record of their feelings and the events of the day so that they can then together go back over the events of the week and try to discern if there is a pattern. Other people find it invaluable to write a journal of their feelings and experiences in order to better understand their responses to life. Both of these work very well with mood tracking.

In essence, mood tracking, or journaling as it's also sometimes called, is keeping a diary. However, this is a

"SOME FIND IT INVALUABLE TO WRITE A JOURNAL OF THEIR FEELINGS TO BETTER UNDERSTAND THEIR RESPONSES TO LIFE"

diary of emotion. You keep track of your feelings throughout the day and the week by making a record of them. In order to understand how the world affects your emotions, it's also necessary to note the main details of the day, too.

The key part is simply keeping the record. Some people just write it down in a daily diary. Others write post-it notes, or record an account of the day's feelings on their phone. Nowadays, people also employ spreadsheets or apps. As it can be difficult to put feelings into

words, particularly at the start, a mood chart might be helpful for identifying different emotions. Some idea of the level of the emotion is often useful, which can be done by writing next to the feeling an intensity scale from 1 to 10. With generalised anxiety disorder, a careful record of periods of heightened anxiety and panic attacks is particularly important.

Like keeping a diary, mood tracking is a very personal approach to dealing with anxiety, suitable for some people but not for others.

MEMORY GAMES

Sometimes, distraction can be your friend

The cycle of anxiety is perpetuated by distraction. Anxiety before writing an important essay can be relieved by looking at cat videos on YouTube, the instant release of tension brought through procrastination leading to a further deepening of the cycle. However, there are times when feelings of anxiety can become so overwhelming that simply relieving them becomes more important than anything else. In these cases, effective and non-harmful distraction techniques can be both helpful and necessary.

Among the most effective of these are exercises that intensively use the most conscious part of our brains, the pre-frontal cortex. This is also the part of the brain that is most prone to worry as a mental behaviour, so finding something else for it to fixate upon can allow the rest of the brain to slowly relax.

Any mental exercise that is sufficiently demanding to require complete attention but is not too demanding to overtax a mind that is at its limits is ideal. Many people find memory games useful, whether that be reciting memorised poems or learning something new from scratch. Visual thinkers might try to remember and visualise something familiar: the kitchen worktop, the face of a loved one.

More physical mental games, from jigsaws to Sudoku, can also be effective, as can the many online games. However, as a general rule, high-intensity computer games should be avoided as these will increase stress levels.

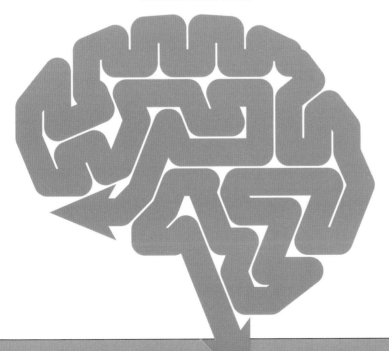

RAINBOW GROUNDING

Using colour to get back on track

Rainbow grounding is a relaxation technique that works particularly well with anxious children. The pandemic and the government response to it produced major increases in anxiety among children so this might be a useful exercise to help an anxious child.

Again, it is based on moving attention out from the internal world to the world around us. Look around and try to see the rainbow in the colours of the things in your surroundings. Start with red, then move through the other colours, yellow, green, orange, purple and blue. It's probably best to skip indigo as most people are a bit vague as to how indigo differs from purple.

As you see each colour, really look at it to see what shade it is, its texture, the way the light falls upon it. It's perfectly all right to add non-rainbow colours to the list too, such as pink or black or grey or brown.

The best thing about this technique is its simplicity, which makes it particularly suitable for young children.

GETTING WET

Use your hands

One of the simplest ways of getting out of one's head is to put your hands in water. Simply plunging your hands into a bowl of water produces an immediate physical effect that pulls us out of the anxiety loop. As your hands go into the water, note the accompanying sensations; feel the temperature of the water and the sensation of liquid on the skin. Some people like to use warm water first and then cold water. Others prefer the opposite. But with both, the key is to put one's attention into the sensation. Accompany the immersion with controlled, even breathing, breathing in for a count of four and out for a count of four. If the water is too cold, this might be a challenge, so it's best not to use iced water.

DANCE OFF

Burning off the adrenaline before calming the mind

Sometimes the physical effects of a panic attack are so severe that it is impossible to focus the mind sufficiently to employ any of the above techniques. The amygdala is pumping so many hormones into the body that it is completely wired, trembling with the sort of energy necessary to outrun a lion or fight off a hyena. With so much physical energy coursing through the system, some people find it necessary to burn off some of the adrenaline first. This can be done by anything from dancing wildly around the room, to running along a corridor or up and down the stairs, or using a treadmill. For other people, something a little more gentle works better – some people have even reported that brisk hoovering or manic cleaning burns off the nervous energy while doing something useful, too. But it could be that going for a brisk walk in a park, or doing some gardening, is sufficient. We all have different thresholds and everyone trying to deal with anxiety and panic attacks has to find what works best for them.

Once the physical activity has taken the edge off the physical response to anxiety, it is time to employ one of the more mental techniques to slowly convince the lizard brain that it can switch off its emergency response and go back to dozing in the sun.

PROFESSIONAL
THERAPIES
AND TREATMENT

Whether to ease recurring symptoms or pinpoint major underlying issues, these methods can target and control anxiety disorders

WORDS AILSA HARVEY

Seeking professional help for anxiety might seem like the hardest leap to take. While you're battling to regain control of your body and its consuming mental and physical feelings of anxiety, surrendering more control to a professional can be daunting.

However, approaching a mental health expert and allowing them to make the best decision for your anxiety disorder can ensure that you take back greater control of your life in the long term.

There are many therapies and treatments that are designed to reduce the symptoms of anxiety. The three main types are medication, psychotherapy and daily management. If anxiety is a regular part of your life, a combination of these methods can be used together to transform your quality of life.

Knowing the personal triggers for your anxiety attacks means that you can try to manage your exposure to them. However, this pressure alone can sometimes impact your mental health further. With the help of professionals, it's possible to take the driving seat in your life – to delve into the root causes of your anxiety and establish longer-lasting ways to put anxiety in the back seat.

WHEN & HOW TO SEEK HELP

If you are concerned by any changes in the way you think or feel, this is enough reason to consult your GP. There are numerous solutions to limiting anxious feelings, no matter how small they may seem. If it is big enough to impede your life or mental wellbeing at all, a GP is likely to be able to share beneficial measures you can take. These could be as simple as introducing minor lifestyle changes

HYPNOTHERAPY

What is the aim of this alternative treatment?

During a session, participants enter a state of mental relaxation and focus. While less research has been carried out on the effectiveness of hypnotherapy when compared to psychotherapy, it's thought that if someone can achieve a mental state of relaxation resembling sleep, the mind becomes more receptive. Depending on what a patient wishes to improve, suggestions will be made during the hypnosis that will reduce their anxiety in specific events. For example, if you had a phobia of animals and it was triggering anxiety symptoms, the hypnotherapy would focus on your perception of the animal. A therapist would target your subconscious to reprogram your thoughts surrounding the animal. In some instances, people have claimed that their mental response to their phobia changed after these sessions.

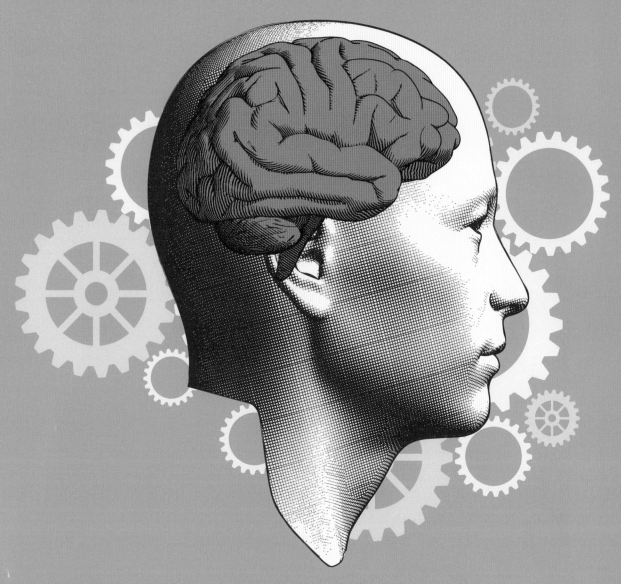

COGNITIVE BEHAVIOURAL THERAPY

How does this treatment tackle negative thought cycles?

Sometimes it can be difficult to pinpoint the core cause of anxiety by yourself; it can actually be easier for someone else to detect unhelpful thoughts. The multitude of feelings that can arise are often overwhelming, but cognitive behavioural therapy (CBT) can help in some instances. CBT sessions involve speaking to a trained therapist to break down the negative thought cycles that result in anxiety, and tackle personal aspects. During these sessions, questions will be tailored towards finding an individual's problematic thoughts. Then, therapists will explore ways to deconstruct these thoughts and reconstruct them for a more positive outcome.

The main concept behind CBT is that situations, thoughts, emotions, physical feelings and actions are all connected. The aim is to change a person's mental approach to daily situations to reduce the likelihood of events developing into anxious feelings.

CBT is one of the most successful treatments for generalised anxiety disorder, as it provides practical solutions to daily struggles. The treatment itself can involve between five and 20 one-hour sessions, but the mental techniques learned in this short space of time can assist you for life.

CBT is only effective if you are ready to be vulnerable and fully confront deep feelings. Underlying issues won't be explored in much depth, such as past events that may have caused anxiety, but CBT equips the patient to better navigate situations in the present.

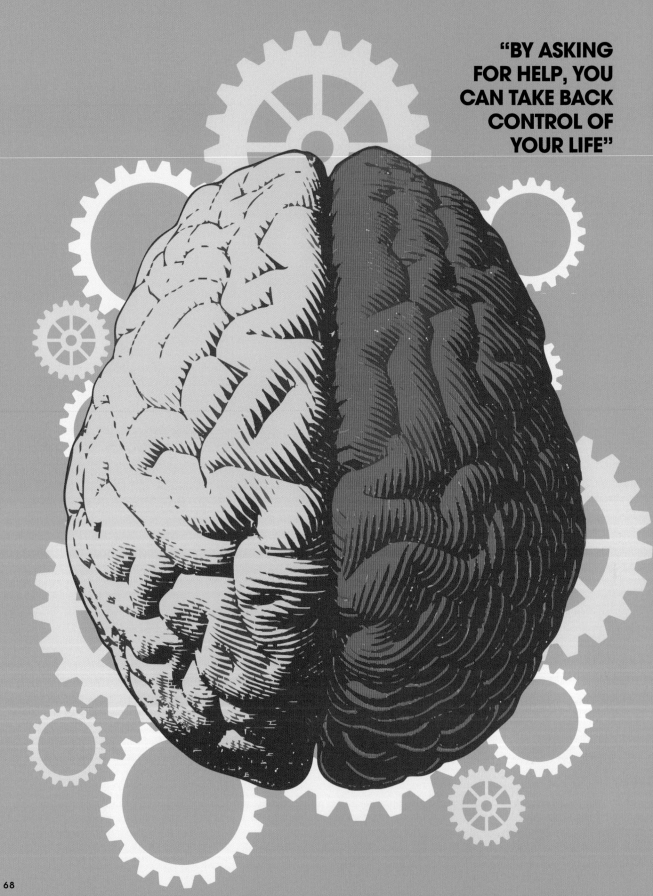

"BY ASKING FOR HELP, YOU CAN TAKE BACK CONTROL OF YOUR LIFE"

that result in noticeable improvements in your mental health. Advice such as limiting your caffeine intake, adding an active element to your day or learning new breathing techniques could ease some feelings of anxiety.

When the symptoms of anxiety escalate to the point that you are withdrawn from social activities, regularly experience feelings of dread, detachment and irritability, or often feel physically panicked in situations, your GP may suggest trying new medication. You may also be referred to a mental health professional, such as a trained therapist.

Considering speaking to someone you don't know about your anxiety can actually create mental hurdles, especially if you're already feeling more anxious than usual. After all, how are you meant to tell a stranger how you feel if you aren't entirely sure yourself? In most cases, the questions that a GP will ask you about your thoughts will help you to process your feelings in ways you hadn't considered before. While this is new for you, health care professionals have the experience to know which

MEDICATION

To relieve the symptoms of anxiety, drugs can alter chemicals in the brain

Medication for anxiety doesn't cure these disorders, but has the power to transform the life of someone who is suffering from one. By managing the symptoms of anxiety, medication helps a person to feel more like themselves and function better. There is a diverse selection of medication available, so, if you suffer from anxiety, you should consult your doctor to find the best option for you. You may need to test out more than one before finding the best solution for you.

Anti-anxiety medication usually works by increasing the mood-altering chemicals in the brain. For short-term treatment, a sedative called benzodiazepines can be taken to relax both muscles and the mind. Because this medication is a sedative, it can cause drowsiness and issues with balance or memory, so it should only be taken for the short period it is prescribed for. There are different types of benzodiazepines for anxiety, but be warned: Xanax is deemed to be one of the more dangerous. Some people develop a dependence on Xanax, and sudden withdrawal from it can lead to lethal seizures. To avoid developing dependence on benzodiazepines, the dosage should be reduced gradually if this medication has been taken for two weeks or more.

Increasing the levels of serotonin in the body can be achieved through medication called selective serotonin reuptake inhibitors (SSRIs). Serotonin is a neurotransmitter that helps to regulate mood and anxiety, amongst other things. Dosage of SSRIs usually starts low and is built up to get used to the medication, because side effects differ between people. These include nausea, excessive sweating and drowsiness.

Some of the physical effects of anxiety are targeted with beta blockers, such as propranolol. This medication works to prevent event-related anxiety attacks, which are brought on in stressful situations. By blocking norepinephrine and epinephrine (adrenaline) from taking effect, this medication prevents reactions such as tightness in the chest and rapid heart rates.

EXPOSURE AND RESPONSE PREVENTION

How can fighting OCD compulsion help reduce anxiety?

This is one of the most effective forms of treatment for people experiencing obsessive compulsive disorder (OCD). OCD is an anxiety disorder that causes recurring thoughts or repetitive behaviours that can't be controlled. Exposure and response prevention (ERP) is a form of behavioural therapy that intentionally triggers a person's obsession and attempts to control it in a safe environment. For example, some people with OCD develop compulsive rituals. To an observer these may seem like small acts, but if the sufferer doesn't carry out the specific ritual, their anxiety builds. If somebody has an OCD ritual whereby they need to lock and unlock a door a certain number of times, they will be challenged to not do this in an ERP session. By asking them to walk through a door and refrain from carrying out their ritual, they will need to use the session to work on controlling the resulting feelings. At first they may be overwhelmed with anxiety, but each time they are exposed to this situation, the anxiety can lessen.

"ERP INTENTIONALLY TRIGGERS OCD IN A SAFE ENVIRONMENT"

EXPOSURE THERAPY

What happens when you come face-to-face with your anxiety?

Exposure therapy is a technique that can be used to combat both generalised and social anxiety disorders that are focused around specific phobias. Psychologists aim to reduce the anxious feelings that emerge in individuals when faced with a phobia by subjecting them to their phobia. This might sound counterintuitive and damaging, but research shows that experiencing your biggest fear in a controlled environment reduces the negative responses felt when the situation is repeated elsewhere.

Exposure therapy doesn't have to involve real-life exposure, but it can. You could be asked to perform in front of an audience if you suffer from social anxiety, or instructed to interact with your phobia. Imaginal exposure, on the other hand, could be centred around a past traumatic event that causes anxiety attacks. Being asked to recall this negative experience can help someone to rethink the events and face their fear mentally.

By completing these tasks in a safe space, people find that they gain confidence around their phobia through better understanding and familiarity of it. Demonstrating that they are capable of navigating the situation shows them that they can do so again if they need to. In other instances, the negative associations they held with the object or activity they were exposed to, and the resulting anxiety, are reduced.

APPLIED RELAXATION THERAPY

These methods help you to gain control of your body

Relaxing may seem impossible during extreme anxiety, but learning relaxation techniques to reduce muscle tension and slow your breathing can help to reduce the intense sensations of this disorder. Knowing effective methods to regain control over your body can be life changing if you regularly experience anxiety attacks.

Applied relaxation therapy includes a wide array of mind-body exercises that aim to calm the body's fight-or-flight response. As everybody is different, it's worth testing out a few with a therapist to find the technique that best allows you to relax. However, relaxation might not work at all for some. By actively trying to stop the effects of anxiety when you are most distressed, you might send additional signals to your brain that you're in danger. If this happens, your body's uncontrolled defence response could increase or remain high. In this case it is best to use these techniques when you are not at your most distressed.

Some examples of techniques that you can try are slow diaphragmatic breathing and progressive muscle relaxation. To achieve deep breathing, inhale and exhale slowly, while avoiding lifting the shoulders. You should place one hand on your upper chest and the other below your ribcage. Focus on each breath pushing only your lower hand outwards. This strengthens the diaphragm and relaxes the body.

To feel the benefits of progressive muscle relaxation, tense any muscle for 15 seconds. Then, release the muscle and count to 30. When this works well, you should feel the sensation of relaxation pass through your body.

EYE MOVEMENT DESENSITISATION AND REPROCESSING

There are conflicting opinions on the success of this relatively new method

Research shows that eye movement desensitisation and reprocessing (EMDR) can reduce feelings of anxiety when recalling a distressing past event. Many health care professionals believe more research needs to be conducted on this form of therapy, while others say they have witnessed its success.

The therapy involves the patient recalling their emotionally charged memories while focusing their eyes on the therapist's finger. As the individual speaks of the event, which is usually avoided due to feelings of anxiety, the theory is that they change how the memory is stored. Because they were focusing their attention on their eye movement, they feel more comfortable mentally revisiting this traumatic event in the future.

While experts are unsure exactly how the results unfold, this method has reduced the intensity of psychological responses for many individuals when they later retrieve anxiety-inducing memories.

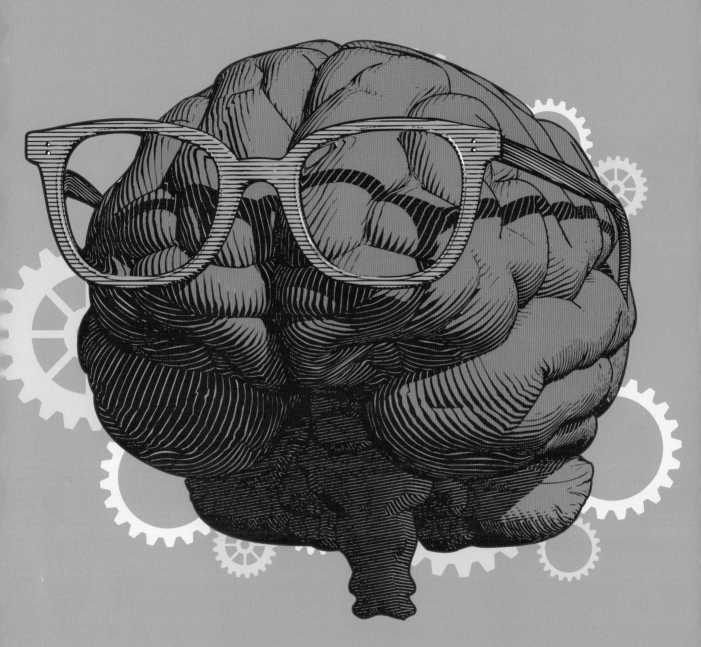

type of treatment you are most likely to benefit from. Taking the first step and asking for help means you gain guidance, and the pressure to find the answers by yourself disappears.

"MOST IMPORTANTLY, TRY TO BE AS OPEN AND HONEST IN YOUR APPOINTMENT AS YOU CAN"

Before your appointment, you may want to write down any questions you have, or new feelings you have experienced. This will give you reassurance that you won't forget to mention specific aspects of your anxiety or ask a question that comes to mind during the lead-up to the appointment.

Most importantly, try to be as open and honest in your appointment as you can. Time with GPs is often limited, but this time is crucial for

them to gauge a true picture of you and your mental health.

At the end of the appointment you could be given some at-home methods to reduce anxiety, a prescription for anti-anxiety medication or a suggestion for a specific therapy type. If you are unhappy with the advice given, you are within your rights to request a second opinion. Additionally, if you are only given medication, you can ask which talking therapy options are available to you.

THE TALKING THERAPY THAT WORKS

Cognitive behavioural therapy is the standard treatment for anxiety for a very good reason

WORDS EDOARDO ALBERT

Back in the 1970s, when cognitive behavioural therapy (CBT) was first developed, the practitioners using it had an in-house name for what they were doing: 'the talking therapy that works'. CBT was by no means the first psychotherapy to be developed. By then, there had been more than 80 years of treating mental health problems through conversation. Modern psychotherapy began in the late 19th century when Sigmund Freud developed psychoanalysis and during the 20th century many new types of psychotherapy had been developed, including psychodynamic therapy and person-centred therapy.

However, while there had been a flowering of psychotherapies, there had been relatively little work done to assess just how effective they were as treatments. Clinical experience suggested that they worked but the question remained how much this was due to the therapy and how much was down to other factors. After all, a full course of psychoanalysis could take ten years and involve weekly or twice-weekly hour-long sessions with the psychoanalyst throughout that time. Critics argued that simply having someone to talk to who was willing to listen to whatever you had to say – the foundation of psychoanalytical therapy was free association, meaning that the client should speak on whatever came

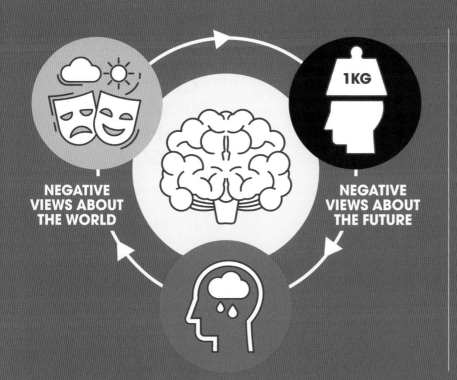

NEGATIVE VIEWS ABOUT THE WORLD

NEGATIVE VIEWS ABOUT THE FUTURE

NEGATIVE VIEWS ABOUT ONESELF

"NEGATIVE VIEWS ABOUT ONESELF LEAD TO NEGATIVE VIEWS ABOUT THE WORLD"

into their mind – for that length of time would have a beneficial effect on its own. Similar criticisms applied to the other talking cures.

One of the psychiatrists aware of these criticisms was Aaron Beck (1921-2021). As well as his medical training in psychiatry, Beck had also qualified as a psychoanalyst. In his practice as a psychoanalyst, Beck became increasingly doubtful about the main tenets of psychoanalysis (which was by far the most common

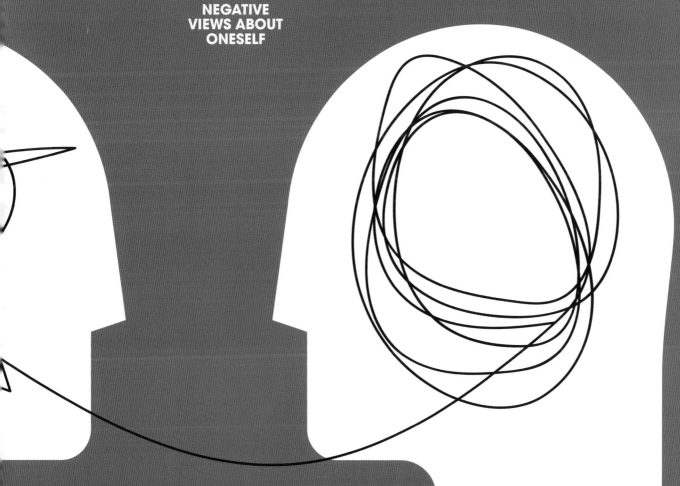

form of psychotherapy in the mid-20th century). As a particular catalyst for his doubts, Beck told of a patient whom he had been seeing for a year. When he gave her the standard psychoanalytic explanation for her anxiety – that her sexual impulses were clashing with her ego – the patient answered that actually she was feeling anxious because she was worrying that she was boring and that she thought this with everyone.

Beck had found with other patients that they often reported a constant stream of negative thoughts. It was like an internal scold was always telling them off. The thoughts covered three areas: the patients' own self, the world and the future. Beck realised that this cognitive triad formed a reinforcing negative feedback loop, where negative views about oneself led to negative views about the world and the future.

Typical examples of the sorts of recurrent thoughts that are characteristic for each of the vertices of the triad include: "I'm repulsive and worthless" for views of the self,

"No one loves me" for views of the world and "I will never succeed no matter what I do" for negative views of the future. Each vertex of the triad reinforces the other two vertices. For example, believing that I am worthless leads to believing that no one loves me leads to believing that I will never find a spouse because why would anyone want to marry someone as repulsive as I am. Having identified these recurring negative thoughts, Beck began working with his patients, trying to help them think more accurately about themselves and their situation. He did this by first getting them to identify the negative thoughts and then to examine them. Was it really likely that absolutely everybody found everything the lady said boring? Just saying it out loud revealed that the thought, which had become a belief by repetition, was ridiculous. Having identified these faulty thoughts, Beck's clients not only began to feel better but they began to change the behaviours associated with their negative thoughts.

Aaron Beck was on the verge of creating a new type of psychotherapy.

"UNLIKE PREVIOUS TALKING THERAPIES, CBT DOES NOT FOCUS ON WHAT HAPPENED IN A PERSON'S PAST"

It seemed that embedded distorted thinking had a deep effect on people's behaviour. For instance, thoughts of personal worthlessness led to withdrawal from social interactions with other people, which led to social isolation, which therefore provided further evidence for the accuracy

of those thoughts of personal worthlessness.

Looking at the nature of these distorted thinking patterns, Beck identified six main pathways by which the distorted thinking became embedded. These were:

Magnification: making bad things worse than they really are.

-

Minimisation: downplaying good things.

-

Overgeneralisation: coming to a conclusion based on something happening once.

-

Personalisation: saying that you are responsible for events that really aren't under your control.

-

Selective abstraction: deciding based on just one aspect of a situation.

-

Arbitrary inference: coming to a conclusion based on little or no evidence.

As these distorted thinking patterns become embedded in a person's mental pathways, they slowly form his or her core beliefs about themselves, the world and the future. In effect, they become more than patterns of thinking: they become emotional moulds that further embed the thinking patterns.

The second pole of cognitive behavioural therapy, the behaviour part, has its roots in behaviourist theories and therapies that were developed in the first half of the 20th century. Behaviourist thought eschewed the internal mental world of subjects in favour of their behaviour. It originated with Ivan Pavlov's famous work on conditioning, where he found

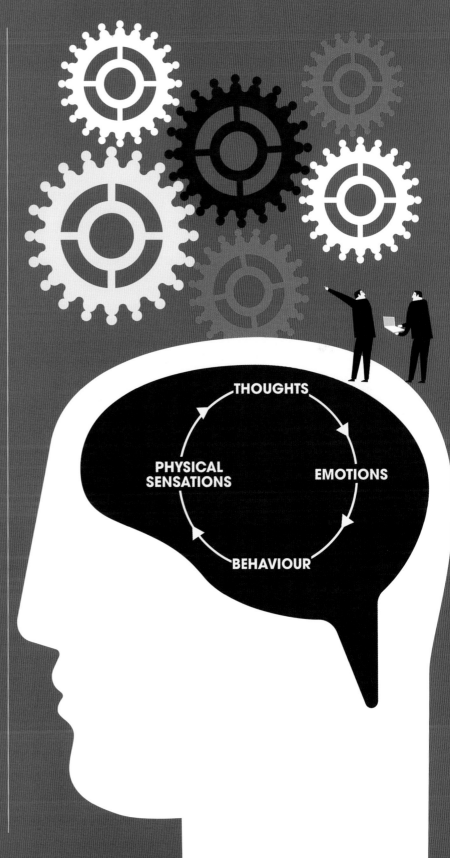

THOUGHTS

PHYSICAL SENSATIONS

EMOTIONS

BEHAVIOUR

that ringing a bell whenever he fed a dog would quickly lead to the dog salivating in anticipation of food when the bell rang, even if no food was forthcoming. B.F. Skinner developed Pavlov's work, showing that operant conditioning, positive and negative reinforcements, could also affect behaviour.

The distorted thinking patterns that Beck had identified in his subjects were affecting their behaviour, positively reinforcing harmful behaviours and negatively reinforcing helpful behaviours. By identifying these distorted thinking patterns, Beck found that he was helping his patients change their ways of thinking and that doing so led to a change in the behaviours associated with these thinking patterns.

By the 1970s, Beck and his associates had developed a new type of psychotherapy – cognitive behavioural therapy – and they and other researchers set out to test whether it worked. In contrast to psychoanalysis and the other talking therapies employed at the time, CBT was short. A typical course of treatment consists of between five and 20 hour-long sessions with a therapist. Again, unlike previous talking therapies, CBT does not focus on what happened in a person's past. While reasons for someone believing they are worthless might come up during the course of the treatment (for instance, that their parents always said they were a disappointment), the focus of the therapy is on the present. CBT is geared towards identifying the

"THERAPISTS ARE HAPPY TO EMPLOY A WIDE RANGE OF TECHNIQUES TO HELP THEIR PATIENTS"

distorted thought patterns and their resulting behaviours and changing these, rather than finding their roots in the patient's past.

Another major difference between CBT and previous talking therapies was its focus on particular outcomes. The patient and the client, at the start of their sessions together, talk through the patient's problems and decide on what needs fixing. What do they

want to happen as a result of CBT? As such, CBT is particularly well suited to defined mental health issues. It works less well with more generalised issues.

Because CBT requires a relatively short course of treatment and because the patient and therapist are seeking defined outcomes, it is easier to measure its effectiveness when compared with other forms of talking therapy. Multiple studies have confirmed that CBT is an effective treatment for bipolar disorders, schizophrenia and psychosis, and is especially effective for depression and anxiety disorders (the two, of course, are often linked).

This is why those early CBT therapists allowed themselves the private shorthand of calling CBT the talking therapy that actually worked. In comparison to therapies such as psychoanalysis, they had the evidence that what they were doing was really making a difference.

Indeed, such has been CBT's success that it has produced a whole slew of related psychotherapeutic practices that use the basic insight of CBT and develop it. Among these developments are dialectical behaviour therapy, which builds on CBT by employing strategies such as the currently highly popular mindfulness meditation techniques, and multimodal therapy, which broadens CBT to include consideration of sensation, imagery, interpersonal relationships and biological considerations.

Now, let's take a look at how a typical course of CBT might proceed. During their first meeting, the therapist will seek to establish from the patient their reason for seeking treatment, what hopes they might have from the treatment and what they desire to be the ultimate outcome. For the course of this example, let's assume that the client has gone to seek help with their anxiety about meeting

STILL WORKING?

Is CBT becoming less effective as a treatment?

In 2015, researchers published a paper that rocked the CBT community to its core. This analysis of the efficacy of CBT treatments over the decades since it was first developed in the 1960s showed that it was becoming less effective. In fact, it was half as effective in treating depression as it used to be. What had started off as the talking therapy that worked was becoming the talking therapy that was not working nearly so well. Not surprisingly, the paper caused a huge uproar. In Britain, the NHS has hugely ramped up training of CBT therapists to make mental health care more accessible, in part because CBT is a defined and short treatment that provides a relatively cheap form of mental health care.

In answer to the paper's findings, some psychiatrists pointed to the huge increase in therapists as part of the reason for the decline in effectiveness. Before, only trained psychologists could provide CBT. Now, a one-year postgraduate course in CBT is sufficient to practise as a therapist. This has produced more therapists but, some practitioners argue, has led to a decline in the skillset of therapists. With the relationship between therapist and patient being key to successful outcomes, they argue that this is responsible for the apparent decline in the effectiveness of CBT.

Another factor may be the placebo effect. When first developed, CBT was hailed as the miracle therapy, the cure that worked. People seeing a CBT therapist, hearing this, believed it would work and this produced a more marked placebo effect. Of course, there is an issue with using the placebo effect in therapies that depend in part upon belief: it's actually part and parcel of the treatment. With less belief in the efficacy of CBT, its effectiveness has diminished.

Another explanation is that CBT has actually been too effective and thus engineered its own decline. According to this idea, psychotherapies are developed to deal with the mental health issues of a particular era. Freud developed psychoanalysis to deal with the aftermath of Victorian repression. By doing so, and with psychoanalysis having been so effective that it put paid to Victorian mores, the efficacy of psychoanalysis declined. The new, post-60s society was not hung up on sex but it no longer had the moral fortitude to deal with behaviours we want to change by pure willpower – hence, the development of CBT. With the success of CBT, society has shifted again, moving towards a new dominant form of psychotherapy: mindfulness.

The question of CBT's declining effectiveness remains open, however. Researchers have called into question the original research, with some finding no change in CBT's effectiveness and others finding that its effectiveness declined between 1977 and 1995, but it has been stable since then.

However, all the researchers do agree that it still works. How much it works continues to depend most of all on the patient and the therapist.

people and speaking in public. In the first session, the therapist learns that the patient's chronic anxiety about meeting people is stopping them socialising with friends or work colleagues, while their fear of public speaking means that they have not been able to advance in their career. Indeed, they fear that their worries about socialising might eventually make them unable to leave her house.

Having established the nature of the problem, the therapist will typically ask their patient to do some homework before their next session together. They might ask the patient to keep a journal of their worries, or to start practising a relaxation technique. Because CBT is a result-oriented psychotherapy, therapists have been happy to employ a wide range

of techniques to help their patients identify and overcome their distorted thought patterns.

One of the ways in which CBT therapists assist their patients in identifying faulty thought patterns is by helping to develop metacognition. This is the ability to think about thinking, to understand how we come to the conclusions we come to. With a patient who is anxious about social situations and public speaking, the therapist might ask them to record their feelings when faced with a social situation and, crucially, the thoughts that led up to those feelings. Returning for the next session, the patient reports that they had been invited to an after-work drink by one of their bosses and had immediately panicked and made an excuse. But examining their thoughts afterwards, they realised that they had gone through a sequence of thoughts that ran: I'm only being asked out because he has to, he's my boss, which became he doesn't really want to invite me, which became no one likes me anyway so I'd better say no so that no one has to have a conversation with me. Simply identifying this habitual pattern of thought is a powerful tool towards understanding and changing it.

Other ways of developing metacognition include asking the patient to ask themselves what is really the worst thing that could happen in a situation and why. As part of the homework for the next session, the therapist might give the patient a thought record, a sheet of paper to record the negative thoughts and behaviours, and the situations that provoked them. A typical thought record will have three columns: the first for the patient to note the situation that produced negative emotions, the second to list the characteristic negative thought patterns that the situation produced, and the third to write down what negative emotions the situation and the thoughts produced.

Having made a start on identifying the automatic thoughts that produce the behaviours the patient wants to remove, the therapist might use some role-playing games in following sessions to rehearse some of the situations that the patient finds stressful. For a patient who panics about public speaking, the therapist might start with something like an exercise imagining speaking to a small

"COGNITIVE BEHAVIOURAL THERAPY WORKS AS A PARTNERSHIP BETWEEN THERAPIST AND PATIENT"

group of people. To deal with social anxiety, the therapist and client might role play small talk at a party. The aim is to provide the patient with a suite of strategies that will enable them to face their social anxiety.

A key part of CBT therapy is the therapist setting the patient attainable goals to try to achieve before their next session together. This is a joint process. It should not just be the therapist saying, "You will do this", but therapist and patient together deciding what is possible for the patient to attempt in the coming week. The mnemonic for these goals is for them to be SMART: specific, measurable, attainable, relevant, time-based.

So the therapist might suggest that before their next meeting their patient should talk to one stranger. The patient might say that this is too much for them at the moment.

A compromise might be reached, with them trying to speak to someone they know only in a very limited way at work. This is important, as CBT works as a partnership between therapist and patient, rather than the therapist acting as an all-knowing director to the patient.

The therapist might also set their patient relaxation exercises. For anxiety disorders, it's important for the patient to practise these between sessions so that they can embed the exercise – it's another example of the homework and goal-based approach taken by CBT.

By the end of their time together, the patient, working in partnership with their therapist, will hopefully have identified the mental thought patterns that were producing behaviours that were unhelpful or distressing. Having identified and recognised these automatic thoughts, they will have developed ways to deal with them, from recognition and ridicule through to replacement by more appropriate mental thought patterns. With the automatic thoughts and their nature recognised, the patient will not be caught in the resulting behaviours and will be able to employ the various strategies worked out in partnership with the therapist to put in place new behaviours.

While this is the general outline of a course of CBT treatment with a trained therapist, some people do try various self-help CBT therapies, working from books and online. Investigations of the efficacy of doing CBT on one's own have shown that it can work, but all the studies indicate that it works better when done with a therapist.

Cognitive behavioural therapy is the most tested form of psychotherapy. It's the recommended form of therapy for people suffering with anxiety disorders because, quite simply, it has been proven to work.

WORRYBOOK

How social media is fuelling anxiety and depression

WORDS EDOARDO ALBERT

n the first half of the 20th century, some psychologists were growing frustrated with what they saw as the woolly nature of the prevailing psychological theories. In particular, psychoanalysis promised all sorts of insights into the depths of human psychology but it had proved almost impossible to test it empirically. For something to be a science, its

"PSYCHOLOGISTS TRIED TO STUDY THE MIND BY IGNORING IT"

predictions have to be testable – you have to be able to do experiments and see if the results match the theory. It's very difficult to do this with psychoanalytic theory.

In reaction, a group of psychologists proposed a whole new way of doing psychology based on the radical step of entirely ignoring what went on inside people's minds in favour of what they actually did, their

"SOCIAL MEDIA IS DESIGNED TO KEEP US COMING BACK FOR MORE"

behaviour. Behaviourism, as it became called, aimed to make psychology the study of behaviour as what people (and animals) do can be seen and directly tested.

Looking back, it might seem ludicrous that psychologists should try to study the mind by ignoring it. But in their favour, these first behaviourists had discovered an important method of learning by which they sought to understand all of behaviour. This method of learning is called conditioning and it was first discovered by the Russian physiologist Ivan Pavlov in 1897. Pavlov found that ringing a bell whenever a dog was given food would soon lead to the dog salivating when the bell rang, even when food did not appear in his bowl afterwards.

The psychologists, in particular J.B. Watson and B.F. Skinner, who developed behaviourism as a psychology, investigated conditioning further and found that as well as the classical conditioning discovered by Pavlov, there were other types. The most obvious is negative conditioning, where a punishment is associated with a stimulus. If a poor dog goes to eat from his bowl and then receives an electric shock from the bowl, he will soon give up trying to eat from it, no matter how hungry he gets.

They also found that the strength of the conditioning, whether positive or negative, depended on the schedule of the reinforcement – that is, how often it happened. Their key finding was that the strongest reinforcement, the conditioning that kept animals and people coming back to do the same thing over and again, was when the reinforcement was set to random intervals. That is, the dog would press a lever and sometimes he would get a treat but there was no way for the dog to tell which press of the lever would produce the treat.

Sound familiar? This is exactly the same principle that makes social media addictive. Post a picture on Instagram, say something on Facebook, make a joke on Twitter. You have no way of knowing when, or if, the responses will come. It's the purest example of what the behaviourists called variable ratio schedule reinforcement. And it's designed to keep us coming back for more.

Here's the bad news. Social media companies, computer game manufacturers, everyone involved in this billion-dollar business knows this and they engineer their products deliberately to make use of this deep-wired weakness in the human response system. Think of computer hackers. They try to get into a computer by exploiting some weakness in its operating system and the most vulnerable areas of the operating system are usually the oldest, the bits upon which all the newer stuff has been bolted.

A mind hacker, trying to get into our skulls, would look for the oldest, deepest-rooted responses in our brain, those that go back to our evolutionary past. These are the basic fear, flight responses and the basic conditioning responses – despite all our knowledge and culture, the smell of bread baking still makes our mouths salivate and our tummies hungry. Our deep past as a species is social. In Africa, our ancestors could only survive as part of a group. On the savannah, expulsion from the group meant death.

Our desire to belong is so profound because it comes from a time when it was literally a matter of life and death.

One of the ways that evolution wired sociability into us was to make it pleasurable. A smile, shared laughter, all the intangible aspects of friendship and love set off little pleasure bombs in our brains. These pleasure bombs are little bursts of dopamine, a chemical produced when something good happens and we are joyful. Have you ever had a surprise party that was a genuine, jaw-dropping surprise? If you have, it's pretty certain that you remember that party more than other parties that you spent weeks planning. This is because unexpected pleasures trigger a much greater response from our brain. It's intermittent reinforcement and it gets our brains firing like nothing else.

Suppose you play the lottery and every single time you play you win £10. It's good. You're investing a pound and making ten. You would keep doing it but it wouldn't be long before it becomes mundane. Buy lottery ticket, here's my £10. The whole gambling industry rests upon intermittent reinforcement. Sitting in front of a slot machine with all the lights flashing, you put in your coin and you don't know what will come out – a few coins, nothing at all or the jackpot. "It could be you." That was the old advertising slogan for the National Lottery. It almost certainly won't be. But the principle of intermittent reinforcement keeps people coming back, thinking, "Next time."

But it's not just money. Our brain responds with the same alacrity to anything new, and it responds more vigorously when what is happening is unpredictable. The buzz from your phone alerting you to a response to your last post on Facebook, that buzz wires into the deepest, oldest parts of our brain – and it is designed to do so. Social media platforms are social

"A STUDY FOUND TEENAGERS WHO USED SOCIAL MEDIA THE MOST SUFFERED MORE FROM ANXIETY"

validation feedback loops, produced so that the validation they produce is intermittent and thus conditions the most powerful responses possible deep in our brains.

It's no wonder people are wrestling with them. At the moment, researchers are still struggling to cope with the profound changes in behaviour produced by social media in so short a space of time. Facebook only began in 2004. Eighteen years is barely a heartbeat in history, yet it and other social media programmes have produced a revolution in the way people interact with each other. It will take years to truly identify their effect. But the studies that have been completed so far show that there is much to be concerned about and that among the people most vulnerable to the drawbacks of social media are those who suffer from anxiety disorders.

WHY DON'T YOU...

...switch off your phone and do something less boring instead

Studies show that reducing social media use brings significant reductions in anxiety, depression, loneliness, insomnia and FOMO. Here are some ways of cutting back.

Never bring your phone to bed. Leave it to charge elsewhere.

Turn your phone off when you're doing something else. When you're meeting people, driving, exercising or at a restaurant, turn your phone off. Concentrate on what's in front of you, not on what might be on your phone.

Track your use with an app. See how long you spend on social media during the day, then decide how long you want to be on there.

Turn off notifications. That buzz has been designed to pull us out of everything else we are doing and attend to its call. Switch if off.

Set regular check times. If you *have* to check on social media, set particular times when you will look rather than compulsively checking it.

Remove social media apps from your phone. Our phones are our constant companions. Deleting the apps will free us from most of the compulsion to attend to them, while allowing us to still engage at times of our own choosing through a computer.

"IT'S HARD NOT TO FEEL ANXIOUS ABOUT LIFE WHEN CONFRONTED WITH OTHERS APPARENTLY LIVING THE DREAM"

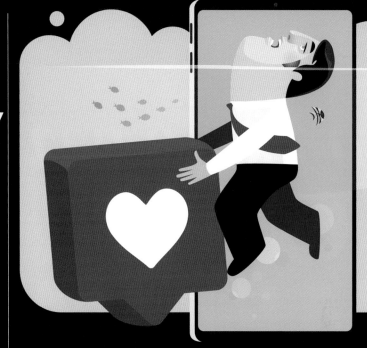

For example, a study published in 2019 had followed a group of teenagers over four years, measuring their anxiety and depression at the start of the study and at its end, as well as how their usage of social media changed during the course of the four years. The study found that the teenagers who used social media the most suffered more from anxiety and depression than those who used it less and, crucially, that their anxiety and depression worsened during the four years of the study. The old rule applies: correlation is not causation. One thing happening at the same time as another does not prove it caused the other thing to happen. But the fact that measured anxiety and depression worsened during four years of intense social media use can certainly be seen as evidence of a relationship between the two.

While intermittent reinforcement is the key driver to social media engagement, it has also greatly worsened another source of anxiety: the fear of missing out (usually shortened to FOMO). FOMO is the worry that other people are having a wonderful time and we aren't. Somehow or other we have been excluded from their picture perfect, carefully curated lives and we look at each immaculate Instagram post and wonder why our lives can't be like that. FOMO drives compulsive social media use, use that is exacerbated by the 'always on' nature of modern communication: the little vibration from the phone that we can spot even through the noise of a party and instantly attend to, despite there being so much going on around us.

To make matters worse, while social media is supposed to connect us, there is considerable evidence to show that the social connections it fosters are shallower, less satisfying and less health-giving than in-person social interaction. In old age, loneliness is one of the biggest predictors that someone will die sooner rather than later. It is human company that keeps us going.

Perhaps the most toxic part of social media is the way it can exclude people. It can do this explicitly, through dismissive or rude comments under an Instagram post, or implicitly, when a Facebook message is met by yawning silence. For people suffering from anxiety disorders, either response can be deeply damaging. Since the internet is so often anonymous, it is much easier for people to leave negative responses in a way that they never would when speaking to someone face to face.

Excessive social media use is driven by the same sort of negative feedback loop that drives anxiety disorders. People tend to use social media more when they are feeling bored, anxious, lonely or depressed as a way of connecting to other people. However, the use of social media tends to exacerbate precisely those negative feelings. It's hard not to feel more anxious and depressed about one's life when confronted with other people apparently living the dream. This therefore worsens the feelings of anxiety, depression and loneliness, leading to further use of social media. It's a vicious cycle and a difficult one from which to break free. In the box (see p85), we shall look at ways to help you cut down on social media usage.

BREAK UP WITH
SOCIAL MEDIA

Step away from the Likes, the intrusive algorithms and the life comparisons, and discover the benefits of disconnecting from your digital life

WORDS JULIE BASSETT

February 2024 marked 20 years since Facebook was launched. Originally called TheFacebook, the service was designed to be used by Mark Zuckerberg and his fellow Harvard students. It then expanded to other colleges and universities, and eventually, in 2006, to everyone over the age of 13 with an email address. Today, there are around 2.5

"RECLAIM THE TIME TO DO SOMETHING FOR YOURSELF"

billion monthly active users. Nearly 1.7 billion people log in to Facebook on a daily basis, and there's a good chance that you're one of them. Add to that Instagram and WhatsApp (also members of the Facebook family) and you're giving over a lot of your time to the hugely influential conglomerate.

There are many reasons why you may use social media: to catch up with friends, to read news from your favourite brands, to send messages, to interact with common interest groups or to keep up to date with events in your local area. These are all perfectly good reasons to use social media,

but how often do you pick up your phone with no real intention and scroll mindlessly through your news feed out of habit? These social networks keep you coming back for more. The 'reward' system of a Like gives value to the content you post, which in turn feeds an in-built desire to put out more posts and garner more Likes.

And yet, for all its benefits, there is a darker side to social media, one that can have a significant impact on our mental health and wellbeing. The question is: do the positives outweigh the negatives? Is it time to take a step back from social media and find out?

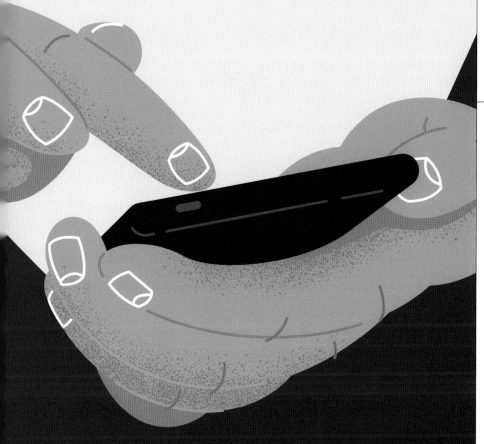

SLIM YOUR SOCIAL ACCOUNTS

Not quite ready to break up with social media completely? There are ways you can gently step away while also keeping a digital anchor. It's important to remember that you are in control of your social media; you can curate your own feed. Facebook, for example, has lots of controls. Set up a Close Friends list and opt for any of your updates to only be shared with those contacts. Similarly, set up a Restricted list, where you can pop all those colleagues and family members you feel obliged to befriend, but don't want to engage with. Next, do a good cull of your Friends list so you're only connected to people you really want to hear from. You can also opt to Unfollow (but remain friends with) people. 'Unlike' the Pages you're no longer interested in, and leave all the Groups you don't participate in. All this will seriously slim down your news feed and can help to make it feel less overwhelming. Similarly, on Instagram you can create a Close Friends list. If following an account makes you feel bad, stop following it. You are under no obligation to do anything on social media – only follow accounts that add something to your day, and that you enjoy seeing content from.

One of the biggest problems with social media is that it can overwhelm us – do we really need so much information available at our fingertips all the time? According to the website NetAddiction.com, information overload is described as 'when you are trying to deal with more information than you are able to process to make sensible decisions'. This is in no way helped by Facebook and Instagram's algorithms, which detect your browsing habits and 'helpfully' suggest other things you might like to see. Read one article on a subject you want to know about, and within minutes you'll be bombarded with suggestions of related pages, products and articles. It can be mentally exhausting trying to process all these different options and tangents, to the point where you find yourself unsure of what to do next, what to buy and even how to think and respond. This 'social media fatigue' is leading to more and more of us opting to take a break from these networks.

A US survey from 2018 found that 42% of Facebook users had taken a break from checking Facebook for at least a few weeks or more, and a quarter had deleted the app from their phone. And in the UK, data showed a slight decrease in the number of UK residents who used Facebook between November 2019 and December 2019.

There are further negatives to our constant social media interaction. For a start, our online profiles aren't truly reflective of our real selves. We tend to curate the information we post and only present the version of ourselves that we want people to see. This can be quite isolating; of our many hundreds of online friends or people we follow, few of them know us intimately in a way that we can connect with them and share our thoughts and worries. We're more connected than ever digitally, and yet far more disconnected personally.

And then there's the problem of comparison. It can be much harder to feel content and happy in your own life when you're presented with picture-perfect daily insights into the lives of other people, who always seem to be richer, happier, thinner and so on. Despite being hyper-aware of how much we want to control our own online appearance, it's easy to forget that everyone is doing the same, and what we're comparing ourselves to is just someone else's presentation of how they want to be seen.

If you do make that conscious decision to break away from social media, then what can you expect? Well, at first, a kind of loss; a worry that you're missing out on something (FOMO!), the fear that you won't get invited to events, or might miss out on the latest work gossip. It will take a little time to build personal connections back up outside of social media, but the benefits of leaving social media behind will surely compensate.

For a start, it frees up time. Rather than mindlessly scrolling apps on your phone, why not reclaim the time to do something for yourself? Read a book, go for a run, hit the gym, paint a picture... all those things you have probably said you don't have time for, despite spending an hour or more a day on Facebook. These things will lift your spirits and nurture your soul. Make actual real-life dates to see friends and catch up over a good meal.

Phone people and have a chat, write long letters, visit family – it can be refreshing to step away from digital communication and build strong, personal connections instead. Having strong relationships and friendships can help ease the symptoms of stress, depression and anxiety.

When you're on social media, you spend a lot of time thinking about the lives of other people, whether you know them or not, which can inflame negative self-talk. By stepping away from social media, you can return focus to your own life. It gives you a

"BY STEPPING AWAY FROM SOCIAL MEDIA, YOU CAN RETURN FOCUS TO YOUR OWN LIFE"

chance to think about your priorities
and to focus on your goals.

Of course, there may be genuine
reasons why you can't or don't want to
give up social media completely. You
can still take a step back and reap some
of the benefits. For a start, delete the
apps from your phone so your feeds
are more than just a tap away. Track the
time you spend on social media and set
a personal goal to reduce your usage.
Turn off your notifications so you
don't have the constant update alerts,
and set aside some days that are free
from all social media.

Give it a go and see how
it feels – there's a real
world out there, waiting
for you to rediscover it.

DEALING WITH PROFESSIONAL ANXIETY

How to recognise and tackle anxiety in the workplace and the classroom

WORDS SCOTT DUTFIELD

Whether it's a project presentation just around the corner, exams on the horizon or dreaded deadlines looming ever closer, the pressures of the working week can sometimes seem too much to handle. Feelings of self-doubt, nervousness and frustration can wash over us in a wave of anxiety that's hard to dry out from.

Between 2020 and 2021, a report by the Labour Force Survey (LFS) revealed that stress, depression or anxiety accounted for 50 per cent of all work-related health issues in the UK. The report also found that the industry with the highest prevalence of anxiety was the education sector.

"MANY OF THOSE THAT SUFFER FROM IMPOSTOR SYNDROME OR FEELINGS OF INTELLECTUAL SELF-DOUBT OFTEN SUFFER ALONE"

The symptoms of workplace or classroom-based stress aren't dissimilar to the other anxiety triggers that life can throw at us. However, in a professional or educational setting, the stakes of feeling anxious can feel particularly great. For those who catastrophise, a commonly associated behaviour with anxiety, the first thought is often the fear of being fired from their job or failing in their studies as a result of their anxieties.

Anxiety can rear its ugly head at any time. Whether it's feeling the mounting pressure of a looming deadline, interactions with co-workers or public speaking, anxiety is an individual experience and affects us all in different ways. However, what unites anxiety is its ability to halt happiness and prevent us from achieving our goals.

One common way that anxiety in the workplace can manifest is in the feeling that we don't belong at our place of work, or, worse, we feel like an impostor in our chosen profession. Impostor syndrome, also referred to as impostor feelings or impostor phenomenon, is the experience of feeling like a fraud and doubting our abilities to do our job.

Many of those that suffer from impostor syndrome or feelings of intellectual self-doubt often suffer alone, too afraid to express their

"ANXIETY CAN PREVENT YOU FROM REACHING YOUR FULL POTENTIAL"

anxieties. This can be exacerbated by some of the many symptoms of anxiety, including isolating yourself from others.

Unfortunately, impostor syndrome is a vicious cycle, often churning through the initial self-doubt, then fear of being 'found out' and, after any success is experienced at work, it is attributed to the diligence applied to the work

under the feelings and fear of anxiety. The best way to tackle this erosion in self-confidence is to remember that achieving perfection 100 per cent of the time is a myth and mistakes are inevitable. Keeping track of your achievements and recording your wins is a great way to remind yourself that you're no fraud.

It's important to remember that anxiety at work or school is by no means solely a product of self-doubt and can also be the response to a workplace environment. Excessive workloads, unrealistic deadlines, difficult colleagues or a lack of clarity in your job or studies can also trigger feelings of anxiety.

Unchecked, anxiety can stand in the way of you applying for a promotion and similarly upon achieving a step up the professional ladder, preventing you from reaching your full potential in a new role.

How to tackle anxiety

Recognising anxious feelings at work or school is the first and foremost requirement of tackling anxiety. Symptoms of workplace anxiety vary from person to person. It can present itself as a constant sense of worry, irritability and lapses in concentration and escalate to more severe symptoms, such as panic attacks, chest pains and sleep loss. Anxiety can also change human behaviours, such as a reduction in appetite, antisocial behaviour and alcohol consumption or smoking as a coping mechanism.

Once you've identified that you want to tackle your anxiety, then it might be time to talk to someone about it.

As the old saying goes, 'a problem shared is a problem halved' and when it comes to anxiety at work or school it couldn't be more appropriate. Talking to your manager, colleagues, educators or classmates can help to solve some of the issues sparking your anxiety, such as addressing workloads or meeting study deadlines. Suffering from anxiety can be an isolating experience, but sharing your concerns and fears can help to alleviate the nagging thoughts

of self-doubt or professional pressure. However, it is important to remember that you aren't required to talk to anyone at your workplace about an anxiety disorder that you may have. Alternatively you could confide in people outside of a professional setting.

Confronting your anxiety head-on is also an effective way of exemplifying your abilities, especially at work. For example, if the source of your anxiety is professional or academic presentations, enrol in an online course in public speaking and push yourself to re-evaluate what you are capable of. Exposure to your anxieties can sometimes be the solution to overcoming them.

There are several practical experiences you can do at your desk to help deal with your anxiety. One of which is called progressive muscle relaxation (PMR). PMR is a type of relaxation method used to lower anxiety, as well as fight insomnia. While seated or lying down, close your eyes and cycle through inhaling deeply through the nose and slowly exhaling from the mouth several times. Next, tense and hold different groups of muscles, starting at the toes. After a few seconds release the tension and move onto another muscle group and work your way through the body, such as the muscles in your legs, abdomen, hands and shoulders, and so on.

"TAKING A FEW MOMENTS TO CHANGE YOUR PACE AND MOVE AWAY FROM YOUR COMPUTER SCREEN CAN HELP TO REDUCE THE OVERWHELMING FEELINGS OF ANXIETY"

If you feel like you need a more involved physical activity to tame your anxious feelings, then perhaps explore quiet meditation, yoga and tai chi, which are great ways to help relax your muscles, lower tensions in your body and teach you useful calming breathing techniques. Spending some time in the morning before work doing these activities as well as taking classes after a working day is also useful time spent to reduce your anxiety levels.

Taking a break and stepping away from your work is also an important way to sever the connection between work and feeling anxious. Taking a few moments to change your pace and move away from your computer screen can help to reduce the overwhelming feelings of anxiety. This may also be a good time to practise some mindfulness meditation for five minutes. Sitting in a quiet place, slowly inhale and exhale, concentrating on

your thoughts. The goal here isn't to completely clear your mind, but simply make note of your thoughts, without getting carried away with them, as an observer. This can help to alter your perspective of your anxious feelings and potentially help to reduce them.

Adopting healthy habits, such as regular exercise, healthy eating and adequate sleep, and concentrating on a self-care routine is also a great way to help to combat anxiety at work.

If any of these self-administered tips and tricks aren't able to subdue your anxiety, then it might be time to pursue professional medical help. There are many different therapies available. For example, cognitive behavioural therapy (CBT) is a form of talking therapy that addresses a patient's situation and helps to produce stress and anxiety. Rather than delving deep into a patient's past, the therapy tackles the issues the patient is experiencing at present. The treatment is used to teach the patients to challenge their feelings of professional anxiety and hopefully change their perspective on the situation. Unfortunately there isn't a one-size-fits-all way to deal with anxiety in the workplace, but combining different coping methods and addressing your mental wellbeing, will give you the best tools required to manage your anxiety.

OVERCOMING
IMPOSTOR
SYNDROME

It's a self-inflicted feeling that holds you back, burns you out and saps your motivation – and it's time to get it sorted

WORDS TRISHA LEWIS

TRISHA LEWIS
COMMUNICATION COACH

Trisha Lewis is a UK-based professional communicator with a special interest in impostor syndrome, hosting workshops and building communities. As an actor, speaker and communication coach, she is passionate about spotting and sorting everything that blocks confidence and connection.

WWW.TRISHALEWIS.COM

There it goes again: that nagging, negative feeling that you are barely getting away with it. Any minute now, they will find out that you are a fraud! You may have done a good job, but that was by fluke more than skill. You might have fooled them into giving you this promotion, but within weeks you will mess up and the truth will be out. It is obvious that you will never be the real deal - not like those grown-up people over there.

But what if your brain is tricking you into believing your feelings represent reality? Do these impostor syndrome feelings stand up to scrutiny?

What is impostor syndrome?

You might have heard the phrase 'impostor syndrome' before, but what does it really mean? The term first appeared in 1978, in a research article by Doctors Pauline Clance and Suzanne Imes. While the original phrase given to this set of feelings was 'impostor phenomenon', the term 'impostor syndrome' became more widely used – perhaps because it's easier to say and spell! The problem with the word 'syndrome' is that it suggests a medical condition, when in this case it is no such thing. It is a feeling that can come and go. It is a brain trick - a 'cognitive distortion'. Doctor Clance said that in hindsight she would have used the term 'impostor experience'.

Terminology aside, what is impostor syndrome? How is it relevant to you? And what can you do about it? The first point to emphasise is that this is about feelings, not an infection or broken bone. We are talking about a self-inflicted feeling. If you are doing it to yourself, it must surely be easy to fix, right? Achievable, of course, but not easy.

With knowledge and practice, you can get a grip on the negative

"SADLY, WE ARE HIGHLY SKILLED AT FEEDING OUR BAD FEELINGS"

effects of these feelings – but never underestimate the power of emotions. In my teens, I had a record (old-school) by Maurice Albert. It was a song called Feelings and it was full of yearning and angst – perfect for the agony of unrequited love. I would play this record repeatedly. Needle off and back to the start. Feelings are powerful, and unfortunately we are highly skilled at feeding the bad ones.

What does impostor syndrome feel like?

To overcome it, you need to be able to recognise it. It's a disconnected sensation – as if you are on the outside looking in. The others have a right to be there, but you don't. It is the gnawing feeling that if you take your eye off the ball – if you stop doing your utmost to be loved, accepted and perfect – then you will be ostracised by a jeering crowd of haters who have discovered the useless or unlikeable you. It is a feeling of embarrassment when people praise you – they are just gullible or polite. It is a feeling of surviving rather than thriving. You are not alone in having these feelings.

Jodie Foster describe it like this: "When I won the Oscar, I thought it was a fluke […] I thought everybody would find out, and they'd take it back. They'd come to my house, knocking on the door: 'Excuse me, we meant to give that to someone else. That was going to Meryl Streep'." However, it might not have been accepted by Meryl Streep. She too experiences impostor syndrome feelings, which

"EVEN THE BEST OF US EXPERIENCE IT. IMPOSTOR SYNDROME IS A HUMAN CONDITION"

COGNITIVE DISTORTION

Impostor syndrome feelings are your brain distorting reality. The father of CBT (cognitive behavioural therapy), Aaron T Beck, coined the term 'cognitive distortion' to describe the inaccurate version of reality and irrational thought patterns that can lead to states of anxiety and depression. Here are some of these 'distortions' that are relevant to the feelings of impostor syndrome.

DISQUALIFYING THE POSITIVE

Giving little thought or value to positive events. Underestimating your value to others. Assuming your success is more of a fluke than a deserved outcome. Feeling awkward when given compliments.

EMOTIONAL REASONING

Giving precedence to emotional negative feelings rather than rational reality. You feel it, so it must be true.

MENTAL FILTERING

Only allowing the negative to get through your filter, and making sure your brain confirms your already present negative beliefs. You always look stupid when you voice an opinion, so that look they just gave you was confirmation of how stupid you are.

JUMPING TO CONCLUSIONS

Going straight to the negative, without passing scrutiny. Acting like a mind-reader and fortune-teller.

MAGNIFICATION AND MINIMISATION

Your failure is huge; your success is tiny. The threat is massive; the opportunity is minimal. You got four out of five on that one item on the feedback form – this is the one you obsess over.

SO WHAT'S THE BEST WAY TO GET BACK TO REALITY?

The pause and reframe tactics that are at the heart of CBT are highly effective tactics to sort your impostor syndrome feelings.

she describes like this: "You think, 'Why would anyone want to see me again in a movie? And I don't know how to act anyway, so why am I doing this?'" But surely it doesn't affect the likes of all-round superwoman Michelle Obama, or acclaimed Love Actually screenwriter Richard Curtis? Yep, them too! Even Albert Einstein described the feeling when he said: "...the exaggerated esteem in which my lifework is held makes me very ill at ease. I feel compelled to think of myself as an involuntary swindler." You see, even the best of us experience this. It is a human condition. Away from the world of the famous, let's look at some feelings that you might recognise:

I feel 'weak' when I ask for help
-
I feel I need to be perfect, or the game's up
-
I feel that I must show proof of my capabilities

-
I feel like I can't be the real me
-
I feel that my achievements are more fluke than skill
-
I feel awkward when given compliments
-
I feel reluctant to take on new challenges in case I fail
-
I feel weary from 'faking it'
-
I feel as though others in my group [business/friends] are better than me
-
I feel anxious when not in control
-
I feel strangely 'alien' a lot of the time – as if looking in from the outside

Do any of these feelings resonate? What if the feelings are left

unchecked?
Some feelings lead you astray, like hearing a car backfire and fearing for your life; or seeing a stranger in a café who reminds you of someone bad, and feeling anger towards them. They are very real feelings followed by responses that make no rational sense. While gut instinct can provide a healthy decision filter, blindly responding to every feeling with an action or decision can lead to negative consequences. Let's look at some of these – this should motivate you to work on reframing some of your impostor-syndrome-fed responses. I like to group the consequences into three categories:

Hide-out
-
Burn-out
-
Freak-out

This probably needs some explaining.

101

"THERE IS NO QUICK FIX FOR IMPOSTOR SYNDROME. THERE IS NO CURE BECAUSE IT IS NOT AN ILLNESS OR BROKEN BONE"

Why 'hide-out'? Think about it: when you are constantly doubting yourself and living in fear of being 'found out', it follows that you might keep your head down, try to blend in, agree rather than express your perspective, or even walk away from new opportunities. You are unlikely to voice your achievements and things you should be proud of – you mistakenly believe that this would come across as arrogant. Worse still, they would think: 'Wow, they are so full of themselves, and goodness knows why!'

Why 'burn-out'? You're trying too hard to please and be perfect. Perfectionism is a big symptom of impostor syndrome. There is nothing wrong with doing a good job, but if you impose ridiculous standards on yourself for fear of falling short and being found out as a fraud, well, you will burn out.

Why 'freak-out'? You become a living pressure cooker, and bottling up all those suppressed emotions is not good for you. That urge to break free and show the world a less filtered version of you… all that effort you make to be accommodating for the sake of being accepted… all that inexplicable fear teetering on the edge of anger… In the pressure cooker of impostor syndrome, these feelings have no way of escaping – until something goes wrong and the whole thing explodes! If you never let off steam, you risk exploding at the wrong time and place, with dire consequences. You erupt in anger during a meeting, you slam a door so hard that it breaks, you hand in your notice in a dramatic outburst… you get the picture. In an ideal world, you want to avoid all these negative consequences. It's time to get your impostor syndrome under control.

Is there a cure?
Unfortunately, there is no quick fix for impostor syndrome. There is no cure because it is not an illness or broken bone as we established earlier. It is a feeling. You can't stop feelings, and you shouldn't attempt to. We feel; we are human. Many of our negative thoughts are there to protect us. We have the same brain wiring as our ancestors did back in our hunter-gatherer days. We need a healthy dose of self-doubt to prevent us regularly running into danger. However, impostor syndrome is not this kind of natural, healthy self-doubt – it is not helpful. It is a trick, an illusion – it is your own brain giving you fake news!

But how do you avoid the negative consequences of impostor syndrome? You need to acknowledge these feelings. Pay attention to them and be aware of how you respond to them. Instead of making knee-jerk decisions that are fuelled by an irrational feeling, use the pause button. It is such a relief when you discover you are in control of the pause button. You own it. The sequence is:

feeling – pause – action

Simple, but so effective.

Your action plan
There is slightly more to it than pressing the pause button, of course. What do you do during this pause? You need to get rational with your emotions. I used to think this was an impossible mix. My background is as an actor – I assumed that being too rational would squash my ability to emote. But I was wrong. Using the pause button is without doubt the top tactic – keep practising and it will eventually become second nature. I found this habit to be empowering. It was a revelation to discover that, by combining emotion with rationality, I had far more energy to drive creative thought and complete projects.

Here is how this works in practice: take the feeling and put it through the rationality filter.
For example:

Feeling: I feel like a useless child in a world of grown-up professionals.
Rationality filter: Am I a child? Is everything about children useless? Who defines the word 'professional'?

Now ask yourself this: How helpful is this feeling? Only then should you proceed with the appropriate action or decision.
In summary:

1. Press pause between feeling and action
–
2. Put the feeling through the rationality filter
–
3. Act on or dismiss accordingly

Although it might feel like a slog to begin with, consciously following this sequence will become a helpful habit.
Here are some other habits to cultivate:

Ask for feedback (even when your brain is telling you to run away)
–
Keep a daily or weekly 'big myself up' journal
–
Allow the unguarded 'you' out to play
–
Talk to others about these impostor syndrome feelings – you are not alone

Knowledge is power when it comes to impostor syndrome – know it, make friends with it and become the boss of it. Give it a name, perhaps even draw your impostor syndrome character. Taking a step back from the nagging, negative chatter inside your head is a good feeling – a relief and a release. I speak from experience.

HOW ANXIETY AFFECTS OUR RELATIONSHIPS

Discover the different ways anxiety can impact on our personal relationships and some of the ways we can manage it

WORDS LAUREN SCOTT

As well as having a negative impact on our own inner world – our sense of wellbeing, self-esteem and confidence – feelings of anxiety can also affect the people around us. Everyone gets stressed from time to time and takes things out on those around them when they don't intend to. However, for anxiety sufferers, our coping mechanisms and behaviours can very quickly strain personal relationships with our friends, families and romantic partners, as well as professional relationships with colleagues.

Anxiety has many unfortunate consequences for everyday life, but it usually causes people to act in two common ways that make maintaining healthy relationships difficult: through avoidance and dependence. We'll explore what both of these behaviours might look like, and how you can recognise and deal with them in your own interactions.

> **"ANXIETY HAS MANY UNFORTUNATE CONSEQUENCES FOR EVERYDAY LIFE"**

What is avoidance?

When you feel anxious or stressed, do you ever find yourself withdrawing from others? Living with untreated generalised anxiety can mean that a person isn't living their life as fully as they want or could do, and that their relationships aren't being nurtured as well as they could be either. Avoidance behaviour might look like cancelling plans, avoiding hanging out with friends and family, and even turning down job opportunities, fun events or social gatherings.

Whether it's colleagues wanting a friendly chat or our partners showing us affection, symptoms of anxiety

take their toll, and can cause us to be irritable and short-tempered in our interactions.

In romantic relationships, it's common for people to distance themselves from their partners emotionally, to try and escape difficult feelings, rejection or vulnerability. This detached behaviour might make you seem cold or uncaring, and leave your partner feeling confused or rejected.

What does overdependence look like?

On the flipside to avoidance, anxiety can also cause some sufferers to become much more needy, clingy and dependent on those closest to them for support. In difficult situations, it's perfectly normal to seek reassurance

"IF YOU'VE GOT SOCIAL ANXIETY YOU MIGHT REALLY FEAR SOCIAL OCCASIONS LIKE PARTIES"

from loved ones, however, being constantly on edge might mean that you're always relying on someone else to make you feel better, without considering the effect that it has on them. Do you ever lean too much on your loved ones, or in the case of romantic partners, blame them for feeling the way that you do?

We know that those with anxiety tend to overthink, or ruminate on the worst-case scenarios – traits which again strain relationships and cause the other partner to feel stressed, pressured or put upon. Particularly in new relationships, if your anxiety is untreated and unexplained to them, it might confuse a partner to find that you're becoming more and more dependent on them. Despite what love

songs might have you believe, it is not our partner's job to 'fix us' or fix our anxiety, but they can encourage any anxiety treatment, therapy or positive coping strategies.

Anxiety in social situations

Social anxiety, or social phobia as it's sometimes known, is a type of anxiety that typically occurs in social situations, and it links very deeply to your social relationships and worrying what other people think of you. According to the NHS in England, you may have social anxiety if you "always worry about doing something you think is embarrassing and find it difficult to do things when others are watching."

Much more than just shyness, if you've got social anxiety you might really fear social occasions like parties or work events, as well as struggling with everyday activities such as work meetings, talking on the phone, or even going shopping.

It's interesting to consider the idea that many anxious people will avoid social situations for fear of other people finding them 'annoying', yet some people will swing the exact opposite way and create a facade of the person they think other people want to see – the joker or life and soul of a party can also be someone suffering with social anxiety, yet they present themselves differently on the outside.

Anxious thoughts around social situations aren't limited to people you already know, and they can become more intense when you have to interact with strangers – from ordering a coffee, to talking to a cashier at the supermarket. Many socially anxious people end up micro-analysing their interactions afterwards, wondering if a comment they made sounded stupid, for example, or whether they should have shared that private thought with a friend.

Talking therapies are thought to be one of the most effective treatments for social anxiety. It can also help to share and explain your anxiety to trusted friends and family, and in some cases, even your manager, so that they have a better understanding of your experiences.

Reliance on drugs for 'courage'

In the same way that we might become dependent on people to relieve our feelings of anxiety, it's common for individuals with anxiety disorders

© Getty Images

107

to depend on drugs and alcohol to alleviate their symptoms.

These substances feel like a good way to calm the nerves and mind in the short term, and alcohol is, unhelpfully, seen as a very socially acceptable way to unwind. However, in the long term, anxiety symptoms will only reappear or heighten when you come down from the effects – as anyone who's ever had an anxiety hangover can tell you. In the very long term, substance use can of course lead to addictions, which make it almost impossible to maintain healthy and productive relationships.

Becoming aware of your behaviour

For a person to change any unwanted or destructive behaviour, they first need to be aware of when and how it's occurring. You might find it useful to start keeping track of your anxiety symptoms, feelings and actions, perhaps using a notebook or note-keeping app on your phone.

At the end of each day, reflect on any avoidant or dependent behaviour that you engaged in. For example, did you pretend not to see your colleague in the office to avoid talking to them? Or did you walk further to a different supermarket where you could use the

self-checkout tills rather than going to a cashier? Being aware of your actions is important. Not so that you can feel bad about them, but so that you can look at little ways to change and challenge them in the future.

Explaining anxiety to your family and friends

Although you should never rely on one person to get you through anxious situations, it can really help to tell friends and family what you're experiencing, or explain what you're scared or anxious about in a given situation. In order to overcome any anxiety-induced behaviours that are wreaking havoc on your relationships and holding you back, you need to – slowly and gently – face the fears and feelings that you are avoiding. If you approach these situations with supportive family or friends, rather than on your own, the process can seem much more doable.

As an example, let's say you're anxious about a huge birthday party that you've been invited to, and want to avoid it by not going. Why not tell a trusted friend who is also attending the party that stepping into that situation is a huge source of anxiety for you, and talk beforehand about what it is that is

making you feel so uneasy. Perhaps it's that you don't know anyone, or you're worried about what to wear. You could arrange to travel to the party together, so that when you arrive and everyone is introduced, you'll have some support.

While it can be great to lean on others in times of vulnerability, you don't want your own anxieties to dominate the conversation or create a strain on others. You're aiming to get to a point where, eventually, you can tackle avoidant behaviours on your own, which in turn, should positively impact your relationships with others immeasurably and bring you closer to fear freedom.

"FOR A PERSON TO CHANGE ANY DESTRUCTIVE BEHAVIOUR, THEY FIRST NEED TO BE AWARE OF WHEN AND HOW IT'S OCCURRING"

STOP
WORRYING,
START
SOCIALISING

Are you more likely to get butterflies at a social event than be a social butterfly? Find out how to burst more confidently out of your cocoon

WORDS SARA NIVEN

Getting an invitation to a party, wedding or night out is something we are generally expected to be pleased about. Choosing what to wear, meeting new people, and the chance to be part of a special event or get together are all seen as positives.

Not everyone feels that way, however. Although a few nerves can be natural, people who experience physical stress-related symptoms, worry about events weeks in advance or avoid them altogether, could have social anxiety disorder, or social phobia as it is otherwise known.

This recognised mental health condition is considered one of the most common anxiety-related issues, and the third most prevalent psychiatric disorder after depression and alcohol dependence.* Defined by mental health professionals as 'persistent fear and anxiety when it comes to social interaction', sufferers feel exposed to possible judgement or evaluation, especially by strangers.

According to Professor Nick Neave at the Psychology Department of Northumbria University, this actually makes some basic biological sense. "As human beings, we evolved from small kin-based groups, where individuals were surrounded by relatives and everyone knew their place in the social hierarchy. In modern times we are faced with anonymous, large complex societies that may involve meeting strangers every day, particularly when it comes to social occasions. This causes anxiety because we constantly have to work out where we stand with them and never know if they mean us

> **"SUFFERERS FEEL EXPOSED TO POSSIBLE JUDGEMENT OR EVALUATION, ESPECIALLY BY STRANGERS"**

harm." In the past, anxiety might have helped us to stay aware of any potential danger, but it can cause daily distress for those struggling with it today.

So how can you deal with nerves ruining your enjoyment of occasions or preventing you from going altogether? It can be useful to consider any specific anxiety triggers. Most of us feel more comfortable in certain situations over others, and there's nothing wrong

(Kessler et al 1994)

HOLD THAT THOUGHT

Challenge your thinking if you recognise the following:

AWFULISING

This is always imagining the most 'awful' outcome. It's one thing to be prepared for not knowing many people, and another to decide that if no one immediately approaches you, you're a total social failure.

....

PERSONALISING

This refers to thinking you are the focus of everyone's attention in a negative way. For example, if a group of people are laughing, you immediately decide they must be poking fun at you, when it is far more likely they are just having fun.

....

ALL OR NOTHING

There's a middle ground between feeling pressure to be the life and soul and not attending at all. You could decide to go and see how you feel after an hour and make a polite excuse if you're struggling. Over time, you may start to feel more at ease in similar situations.

it may be worth speaking to your GP to see if they feel it could be helpful in certain circumstances.

For big events you feel particularly fearful of, it can be useful to work through the situation in your head but instead of worrying about what may go wrong, picture it going well. Visualising yourself greeting people, smiling and even enjoying it can act as a dress rehearsal for the real deal.

Focusing on others can also be a valuable tool. Have a few suitable questions prepared that invite people to talk about themselves. Good listening skills and genuine interest will be appreciated and may help you feel less self-conscious and anxious.

If you find yourself completely overwhelmed in a social situation, the mental health charity Mind suggests a number of breathing exercises and relaxation techniques. Find out more on its website: **www.mind.org.uk.**

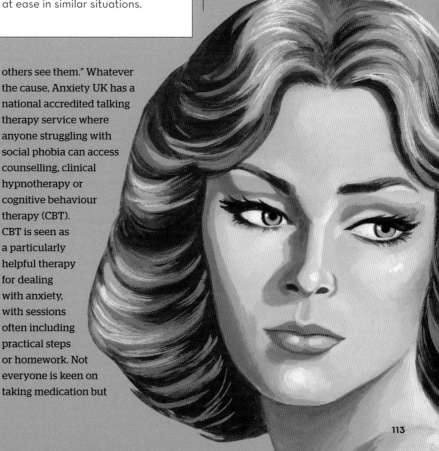

with gravitating towards those we see as a fit, and turning down those we don't. Glastonbury may be out of the question if crowds and camping make you nervous, but perhaps you'd feel more at ease seeing a live band at a low-key event?

If it boils down to fears of being judged, it may be useful to explore any long-held beliefs or conditioning contributing to this.

"People who experience social anxiety often describe their parents as over protective and over critical, which can have a long-standing effect on their social interaction with others," explains a spokesperson for the national charity Anxiety UK. "Equally, some may have been bullied at school, which led them to develop a negative view of themselves and how they perceive

others see them." Whatever the cause, Anxiety UK has a national accredited talking therapy service where anyone struggling with social phobia can access counselling, clinical hypnotherapy or cognitive behaviour therapy (CBT). CBT is seen as a particularly helpful therapy for dealing with anxiety, with sessions often including practical steps or homework. Not everyone is keen on taking medication but

SAY YES

Agreeing to everything may keep others happy, but often at a personal cost. Here's why sometimes saying no means saying yes to self-worth

WORDS SARA NIVEN

Growing up, we are generally taught that saying no all the time is considered impolite. And while young children have no problem using the word freely, sometimes as adults we need reminding of our right to it.

It's one thing to want to help others, but people who feel as though they simply can't say no suffer from an uncontrollable need for approval, and they may have deep-seated fears of anger and confrontation. As the late, acclaimed psychologist Doctor Harriet Braiker points out in her bestseller, *The Disease to Please: Curing the People-Pleasing Syndrome*: "For many, the

difficulty may start innocently enough with genuine and generous attempts to make others happy. But this seemingly harmless passion to always be 'nice', to put others first and to compulsively please them even at the expense of your own health and happiness rapidly spirals into a serious psychological syndrome with far-reaching physical and emotional consequences."

It's obvious that continually adding to a heavy workload because you can't say no to anything risks causing physical exhaustion. But we are less likely to consider how emotionally unhealthy it is too. Always shelving our own needs and desires to meet someone else's sends out the message

that we don't deserve any – both to ourselves, as well as others, who may take advantage. Of course, there are numerous situations where agreeing to things we don't want to do is inevitable. Every parent and most employees will be used to this on a daily basis, and even people with healthy boundaries would find it impossible to say no in such circumstances.

If a teenage son or daughter calls to say they are stranded, safety concerns will override the fact that being woken at 3am to drive into town wasn't on our agenda. For somebody struggling financially, turning down paid overtime may not feel like an option, however much they have on their plate. But if

TO THE POWER OF NO!

there's the expectation you'll drop your own plans (or lose sleep) to provide a regular unpaid taxi service, or to work late every time a report is dropped on your desk at 5pm, learning how to say no gracefully, assertively and firmly is an essential skill for you to master.

For those suffering from the 'please disease', this may take some groundwork and self-examination. First, you need to assess why you continually agree to things you don't want to do. Examine what saying no represents. Is it rejection from social circles? A fear of being disliked, or not doing your job properly? Or perhaps it's concern for being seen as a 'bad' parent or partner? Did you grow up seeing it as essential to toe the line to avoid difficult situations? Remind yourself that self-care is not the same as being selfish, and it isn't your job to take on everyone else's problems or practicalities. If low self-esteem is the main issue, work on this with a qualified counsellor. Then follow our top tips for regaining the right to say no:

Start small. Like any habit, saying yes to everything can be hard to break. Some people will feel easier to say no to than others, just as some things will – start with these and build up.

–

Give yourself time. If your default response is to immediately agree, say that you need to check arrangements. Just don't let this turn into procrastination and guilt.

–

Focus on the positives of a negative and your desired outcome. Saying no to something that isn't a fit for you means being able to say yes to something that is.

–

Be prepared for some people to be taken aback or try to persuade you, particularly if they are used to you agreeing to everything.

Stay polite but firm.

–

Avoid rambling explanations. "That sounds lovely but I have plans on Friday," is enough. As American etiquette expert and author Judith Martin once acknowledged: "Part of the skill of saying no is to shut up afterwards and not babble on, offering material for an argument."

–

Give an alternative suggestion if there's a compromise that works for you, as long as you don't end up agreeing to something else that doesn't. It's pointless saying no to manning a stand at a fête, only to get lumbered with making cupcakes when you don't have time for either.

Finally, if you regularly struggle with how to answer a request or demand, heed this simple line of advice from Brazilian novelist Paulo Coelho: "If you must say yes, say it with an open heart. If you must say no, say it without fear."

MAKE ME TIME A MUST-DO

Feeling frazzled? By making a small amount of time for yourself, you'll be instantly refreshed – and happier

WORDS SHARON WALKER

When did you last have time to yourself? For many of us, we choose to prioritise the chores and tasks of daily life above our own mental and physical needs. You might read this and agree with a frazzled laugh, but this is certainly no laughing matter. Time to unwind is "like fuel in the tank," says psychologist Dr Jessamy Hibberd. "You need 'self-care' to function at your best," she adds. "We're not meant to be doing and thinking all of the time; we're not machines."

Me-time isn't sitting in a bath surrounded by candles (although it can be). Self-care means going for a walk, meeting a friend or staying in bed; whatever you need to reboot.

"Tune in to how you feel and go with it," suggests life coach Jayne Morris. The key is little and often.

DR JESSAMY HIBBERD

Dr Hibberd is a psychologist and co-author of the *This Book Will...* series.

JAYNE MORRISR

Jayne is a life coach and author of *Burnout to Brilliance*.

SUZY READING

Suzy is a psychologist and author of *The Self-Care Revolution*.

Research shows that the resting brain is anything but idle. Downtime gives us time to process unresolved tensions and to gain perspective. Most of us can't simply down tools and nip off to a spa. But it is possible to carve out time for yourself. Here's how.

How to build your 'me-time muscle' in one minute

If you have one minute to spare at the bus stop or between work calls, put your phone on airplane mode and recharge with a hand massage. Stash a tube of your favourite lotion in your handbag and grab a moment whenever you can. First, rub a few drops into your hand to soften the skin. Use your thumb to work into the fleshy heel of your hand, palm side up, then flip your hand over and work into the web

of tendons between your thumb and fingers, moving gently up and down to release tension. Next, move on to the joint at the base of each finger, massaging all the way to the tip. A hand massage is a really good stress-buster for anyone who taps away on a keyboard all day, but it's also the perfect me-time hack if you're standing in a queue or on public transport. "Smell is a powerful mood alchemist," says psychologist Suzy Reading.

–
Tip
Follow your hand massage with a simple breathing exercise, recommends Dr Hibberd. Breathe in for the count of four, hold for five, and out for six... and repeat.

10 minutes

Carve out 10 minutes for yourself by turning any daily activity into a meditation, whether that's taking a shower or getting ready for work. A simple shower can feel like a full spa treatment if you immerse yourself in the experience rather than worrying about to-do lists. Concentrate on the drops of water hitting your skin and use a deliciously uplifting body scrub to add extra zing. Reading suggests you can turn getting dressed into an act of self-care too. Forget grabbing a bunch of scrunched-up clothes from the back of your wardrobe – instead, take ten minutes to lay out your outfit carefully, picking out colours that lift your spirits.

–
Tip
For a relaxing break, eat a square of dark chocolate with a cup of hot tea – and don't do anything else. Focus on the taste, texture and smell, relishing the experience –

"IT'S THE PERFECT ME-TIME HACK IF YOU'RE STANDING IN A QUEUE OR ON PUBLIC TRANSPORT"

117

"PICK SOMETHING THAT'S SPECIAL TO YOU AND WILL TAKE YOUR MIND OFF YOUR WORRIES"

-
Tip
Make a 'happy times' photo album. Try to think about what happened outside the frame, before and after the photograph was taken - research shows that this gives the most uplifting effect. And share the album with the family and friends you were with. This will spark an opportunity to reminisce and boost the bond that already exists between you.

One hour
If you're at home, or work for a forward-thinking company, take a nap. That extra 40 winks will reduce anxiety, boost concentration and increase your energy. You'll also make wiser food choices, improve your memory and think more clearly. Jayne Morris recommends keeping a small pillow in your desk drawer (she used to bed down in empty meeting rooms when she worked for the BBC), and setting an alarm so you don't 'oversleep'. 15 minutes is best, according to sleep researcher Professor Jim Horne; any longer and you could descend into deep sleep and wake up groggy. If you can't make this happen, move your body instead. Go for a walk or try a yoga class in your lunch hour. You can always take a nap in the back row of the class if you're really shattered (another of Morris's 40-winks tricks). "Just warn the teacher you're taking a rest, so they don't worry there's something wrong," she says. If

you work near a swimming pool, Morris recommends a dip as the most nurturing exercise. "There's an association with the womb, when all our needs were catered for, so it feels very soothing."

-
Tip
Block out an hour before bed to create a wind-down routine. Log out from social media, have a bath, listen to music or read. "I write a list of the good things that have happened," says Dr Hibberd. "It reminds you of what you have and helps you appreciate your life instead of worrying about what you don't have or haven't achieved."

and no multi-tasking! If you really must do something, write a list of the experiences, relationships and emotions you are grateful for.

20 minutes
Perhaps you're sitting on the train or waiting for an appointment - now's your chance to master the art of savouring. This is a lovely mind-wandering trick that Suzy Reading recommends, where you simply start to anticipate everything you're looking forward to, whether that's a coffee with a friend, a party or a holiday. You might also want to dip in to your mental archives to unleash some sunny memories. Researchers at Southampton University found that the odd detour down memory lane can significantly lift your spirits, and those who wrote about happy memories were happier after the exercise than those who didn't. But you don't need a notebook to do this, as the biggest mood spikes come by replaying happy memories in your head. "This kind of nourishment is accessible anywhere, at any time," says Reading. Focus on how positive you felt at the time of the experience, rather than how it's over now to stop the memories from feeling too poignant.

© Getty Images

An afternoon

If you're thinking you'll use your free afternoon to clear that email backlog – stop! See a friend instead; it will be better for your health and happiness. "Making time for friends and family is an important part of self-care," says Dr Hibberd. We're social creatures and need relationships like we need air and water. Don't want company? Go somewhere green – and take your shoes off. Yes, really. There's nothing like walking barefoot on the grass to put a spring in your step, believes Morris. "The moment we put our feet on the earth we become more aware of our breath. The deeper we breathe, the clearer we can think." And there's science to back this up. According to research at Harvard Medical School, breathing deeply helps re-oxygenate our cells, which in turn regulates our hormones.

–
Tip
Too many worries running around in your head? "Go to the cinema," says Dr Hibberd. "It's virtually impossible to do anything else at the same time; you can properly switch off and become absorbed in the film."

A day

Take a quiet moment, close your eyes and focus inwards. Now ask yourself what would be the most beneficial way for you to spend your day. "Just see what comes," says Morris. You might want to connect with a friend, or if you're always with people – as working parents often are – solitude might be what you need. Dr Hibberd suggests planning a fun adventure, perhaps a day out to see a new art exhibition or a trip to the seaside. Pick something that's special to you and

will take your mind off your worries. You might want to use the time to reset your priorities. Morris recommends taking five Post-its and writing down the five things most important to you, whether that's work, friends, family or hobbies. Put them in order of importance, then reorder according to the time you spend on each. "People often find work is number one in terms of time, but that might be the least important of their priorities," says Morris. "This shows where things are out of whack and you can spend some time thinking about how you can change your situation."

–
Tip
Block this time out in your diary and tell work and family that you'll be out of reach except for emergencies. That way – hopefully – they'll think twice before disturbing you.

WORRY
EATING

Discover how what we eat can affect how we feel and the ways we can restore balance and combat anxiety

WORDS EDOARDO ALBERT

Are you what you eat? It's an old saying, but increasing amounts of research have shown that it is a saying with more than a little truth in it. But while it's obvious on the physical level, there is a growing body of studies that suggest that what we eat can powerfully affect our mood, too. Anxiety, and in particular generalised anxiety disorder, is strongly linked to depression. A less remarked upon but just as important link is that between anxiety and mood variability. That is, people who have marked and frequent swings of mood are more prone to anxiety disorders.

Scientists have only recently begun to investigate how what we eat can affect our emotions. The answer, it is becoming clear, lies in the gut. The gut is the whole system that starts at the mouth and ends at the bottom, taking

food in and excreting faeces from the other end. Most of the time, the gut does its job quietly and without fuss, leading to it being much overlooked by scientists. But in fact, it's an extraordinary system. For a start, it has its own nervous system: the enteric nervous system. This is entirely different from the central nervous system that we use to consciously control our bodies. The enteric nervous system is the gut's own signalling system, telling the various parts of the gut when food is ready to move from the stomach or pushing the next bolus of digested food down the large intestine.

However, while the enteric nervous system operates independently of our central nervous system, it still needs to communicate with the central nervous system, not least to tell us when we need to stop what we are doing and go to the toilet. That's something that the

gut can't do on its own. It also sends the central nervous system information as to when we have eaten enough, or not enough. The enteric nervous system communicates with the central nervous system via the vagus nerve.

The vagus nerve is the longest cranial nerve in our body. It starts at the brain and goes all the way to the end of the gut. As well as the gut, it communicates with the heart, lungs and the other internal organs. So it functions as a key communication hub in the body,

"THE VAGUS NERVE TELLS THE GUT ABOUT STRESS LEVELS IN THE BODY"

allowing the enteric nervous system to communicate with the other branch of the autonomic nervous system and the central nervous system. The vagus nerve transmits information from the gut to the brain while also relaying information from the brain to the gut. In particular, and this is key to the relationship between food and anxiety, the vagus nerve tells the gut and its enteric nervous system about stress levels in the body.

"INFLAMMATION IS A NATURAL PHYSICAL RESPONSE TO STRESS AND IN ITSELF IS ACTUALLY BENEFICIAL"

This sharing of information goes back into our evolutionary past. The vagus nerve telling the gut about stress levels is one of the ways the body prepares for action. This signalling is why we feel so many symptoms of anxiety in our gut region, from butterflies in the tummy right through to diarrhoea. It's the body getting ready to fight or flee.

But it's not only the body telling the gut that it's time to get nervous. There is increasing evidence that the signals go both ways. What is going on in our gut can have a profound effect on our moods. One of the main ways in which this happens is through chronic low-level inflammation. Inflammation is a natural physical response to stress and in itself is actually beneficial, helping our bodies to get rid of harmful substances and pathogens. However, when inflammation becomes chronic, it can become harmful. There is now extensive evidence linking chronic, low-level inflammation to conditions such as Parkinson's and Alzheimer's.

HEALTHY GUT CHEAT SHEET

Find out what to eat – and what to avoid – to keep your gut happy

FOODS TO EMBRACE

FOODS TO AVOID

There is also strong correlation between chronic inflammation and depression. Depression and anxiety frequently go together – it's hard for someone suffering from chronic anxiety not to get depressed – and while there has as yet been less work on the connection between chronic inflammation and chronic anxiety, studies are beginning to suggest a connection between the two.

If these studies should pan out, and there is every indication that they will, then the gut is where the two conditions meet. Chronic, low-level inflammation is the result of an immune system that is overreacting to stimuli. There are a number of causes for overstimulation of the immune system but one appears to be chronic stress. Chronic, in the medical sense, means ongoing and long lasting, while acute has a sudden onset and usually does not persist.

Chronic stress is one of the causes of leaky gut syndrome. This is where some of the bacteria that inhabit our guts leak out of the gut, where they are

welcome and an integral part of how the gut operates, into the bloodstream, where they are not welcome and where their presence causes low-level inflammation as the immune system acts to destroy them.

The gut is home to a whole ecosystem of bacteria, particularly in the large intestine. It contains ten to the power of 14 (that is a one followed by 14 zeros) bacteria, which is actually ten times more bacteria than there are cells in our body. So for every one of our own cells, we play host to ten bacteria in the gut. We are legion.

It's a mindblowing fact and one that scientists are only just beginning to investigate. But researchers have

"RESEARCHERS HAVE FOUND LINKS BETWEEN WHAT GOES ON IN OUR GUTS & WHAT GOES ON IN OUR MINDS"

ALCOHOL AND ANXIETY

Dutch courage is a dead end

It's a common enough solution: a party, feeling nervous, grab a glass of wine to soothe the nerves. After one or two drinks, everything seems better, you feel looser, more sociable, and you find yourself chatting away to strangers. On the face of it, drinking works.

It works because alcohol is a depressant. It reduces the feelings associated with anxiety, enabling us to go up to strangers and talk to them. It also loosens inhibitions, which means that the sort of anxiety that stops someone letting their real self out is temporarily reduced; suddenly, you become the life and soul of the party, holding forth to all and sundry. It seems like a great success. So the next time you're invited to a party, you have a drink or two before arriving. And when you feel similar nerves before a presentation, another drink then.

This is a classic example of the cycle of anxiety. The stress of a party or other event produces what appears to be a highly effective piece of avoidance behaviour, which reduces anxiety levels. But each time the behaviour is repeated, the habit pattern is grooved deeper, leading to an increase in levels of anxiety and further dependence on alcohol to manage these symptoms. It's a vicious circle and one that is difficult to escape from.

For those people with anxiety, self-medicating through alcohol is a dangerous path – far better to seek professional help.

already found some clear links between what is going on in our guts and what is going on in our minds. Leaky gut syndrome is often caused by imbalances in the gut flora (the name for the collection of bacteria living inside us).

Restoring balance to gut flora can often help to improve leaky gut syndrome. But what is fascinating from the point of view of food and anxiety is that research has shown that restoring balance to the gut also produces distinct changes in mood, with improvements in the emotions that lead to depression, brooding and anxiety. The rebalancing of the gut flora was achieved by drinking a daily dose of helpful bacteria, the 'good' bacteria found in supplements such as Yakult.

Further studies have looked directly at whether improving the balance of gut flora can change stress levels in subjects who are not suffering from leaky gut syndrome. These are people who are subjectively experiencing high stress, from work, family or the usual difficulties of daily life. The studies showed that daily doses of Bifidobacterium bifidum reduced the subjective feelings of stress experienced by the experimental subjects.

Following on from that finding, a further eight-week study fed subjects either Bifidobacterium longum 1714 or a placebo, while measuring the subjects' experience of day-to-day stress. The subjects fed the bacteria were reported,

"CHANGING YOUR DIET WON'T REMOVE ANXIETY, BUT THERE IS EVIDENCE THAT THE GUT DOES AFFECT EMOTIONS"

and were measured via a series of tests, to have experienced a 15 per cent reduction in their feelings of stress.

With stress being the driver of anxiety disorders, any reduction in overall stress should bring benefit to people suffering from them. While a 15 per cent reduction in stress levels is not huge, it is significant, and the improvement comes with little effort: drinking a little bottle of friendly bacteria each day for a few weeks should not be difficult for most people.

Having established that there is a definite route by which what happens in our gut can affect our moods and emotions and therefore act to worsen or ease feelings of anxiety, let us see if there are any specific foods or drinks to avoid or to eat.

Restoring balance to our gut flora is clearly important. Most of the time, the gut flora carry on fine, doing their job quietly and effectively. But for those people suffering from anxiety disorders, it would be worth taking supplements of friendly bacteria following a course of antibiotics. Antibiotics kill off many of the bacteria in the gut. The regrowth of gut flora can be imbalanced, so helping to ensure balance should be beneficial.

Working out from the bacterial gut system, we also know that rapid mood changes can cause stress and thus heighten anxiety. Therefore the sorts of foods and drinks that produce a sudden rush and an equally rapid come down should be avoided: we're looking at you, sweets and fizzy drinks. Other foods that deliver sugar rushes should be avoided, too. The body loves sugar because it is easily metabolised, providing a sudden jolt of energy, but because sugar is so easily metabolised it rushes through our system, leaving an energy void in its wake. And it's not just sugars that do this. Our guts rapidly break down highly processed

LEAKY GUT SYNDROME

Explore the differences between a normal gut and an unhealthy one

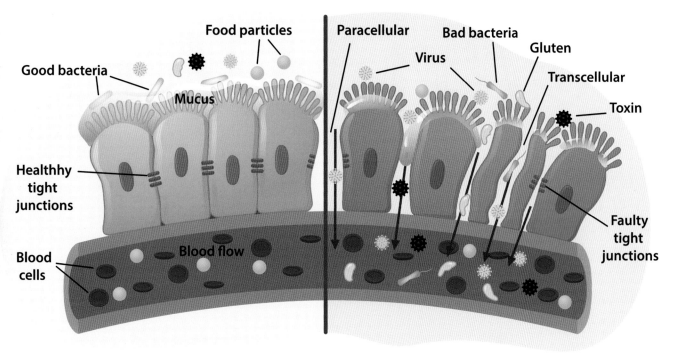

NORMAL GUT

LEAKY GUT

foods such as white bread too, quickly splitting its simple carbohydrates down into sugar. To ensure a more even uptake of energy that lasts longer during the day it is better to eat foods with complex carbohydrates that our guts take longer to break down. These include things like wholegrain bread, brown rice, oats (the traditional bowl of porridge makes an excellent and healthy start to the day so long as it's not sprinkled with sugar but rather drizzled with honey), peas, beans, legumes and vegetables.

Water is also important, as even mild dehydration can cause mood changes. Water itself is the best beverage to ensure hydration. The exact amount you need to drink varies considerably according to the weather. Whatever

the weather though, coffee is not ideal as a rehydrating drink because of its diuretic properties.

Speaking of coffee, and other caffeinated drinks such as tea and most fizzy drinks, caffeine acts as a stimulant so directly affects moods as well as making it more difficult to sleep. As such, highly caffeinated drinks are not ideal beverages for people suffering from anxiety disorders.

The general advice on healthy eating applies to people with anxiety disorders. A balanced diet, cutting down on processed foods, with generous amounts of fruit and vegetables is best. Within the context of a balanced diet, foods rich with omega-3 fatty acids (which basically means fatty fish such as salmon,

sardines, trout, herring and mackerel) have also been shown to help reduce anxiety. Foods rich in antioxidants, such as berries, fruit including cherries, prunes and apples, and vegetables like kale and spinach, may also be helpful as there is some correlation between anxiety and low antioxidant states.

While changing your diet won't magically remove anxiety, there is persuasive evidence that the gut does directly affect emotions. The overall health benefits of better diet will also help to reduce some of the stress markers that produce anxiety. For those suffering severe anxiety, help from medical professionals is still strongly advised but diet can serve as part of a comprehensive strategy to live life better.

EXERCISE
FOR ANXIETY

*Jogging, yoga, dancing...
whatever exercise you choose,
it can really lift your spirits*

WORDS LAUREN SCOTT

While we've known about the physical benefits of exercise for a long time, the positive effects of movement on our mood and mental health are still being discovered. In our stressed-out modern lives, of busy schedules, pandemics and demanding jobs, exercise is often put to the bottom of our priority list.

However, regular exercise is vital for maintaining our mental fitness, too. It can reduce anxiety and stress while boosting our concentration, alertness and even sleep quality. First, let's look at the reasons why exercise of all kinds is so good for reducing anxiety.

It makes sense that diverting your energy from all the things that you're worried about and concentrating on something else can help to clear your mind, avoid rumination and

allow you to see things from a fresh perspective. However, moving your body also decreases muscle tension, which in itself lowers an overall feeling of anxiety. Plus, when your heart rate increases during more vigorous exercise, this triggers a change in brain chemistry to boost the availability of several anti-anxiety neurochemicals, including serotonin.

What kinds of exercises are best for anxiety?

Arguably there's no such thing as the one 'best' exercise for anxiety and the answer will be different for everyone – it all depends on what fits into your current lifestyle. Try to find an activity or sport that is sustainable long term, that you can afford, that makes you feel good about yourself, and in terms of anxiety, is something that will reduce worry and stress, and enable you to feel more positive and in control.

While some of us might find that intense aerobic exercise – think running, circuit training or a cardio gym class – really helps to quell anxiety, for others, getting out of breath and pushing themselves to the limit can actually cause anxiety. If you're looking for inspiration, we'll explore a few popular types of formal exercise here, as well as simple ways to move your body that, in their own way, might help you to find a sense of calm.

Running

Running is of course one of the most commonly touted forms of exercise for beating stress and anxiety, with whole books (maybe hundreds of books) dedicated to the subject. From Jog On: How Running Saved My Life by Bella Mackie to Running Is My Therapy by Scott Douglas, these inspirational stories support the growing body of research that indicate how a consistent running routine can make us happier – or at least, less anxious.

Countless studies have shown that by making jogging a regular part of your life, you'll earn more than just

physical gains (although getting fit in itself can help to build your resilience and emotional toolkit). But what's the science behind the so-called 'runner's high'? And why do people report feeling calmer after pounding the pavements? It's thought that intense exercise increases levels of something called endocannabinoids in the bloodstream – mood-boosting neuromodulators that promote short-term effects such as (hey presto!) reduced anxiety. Running also stimulates the production of endorphins, natural feel-good chemicals that act as mood elevators. This is true of all vigorous exercise, but the effect seems to be more prevalent after a decent jog.

The great thing about running is that there's few barriers to entry. You don't need to join a gym, or run in a team, and you can arguably go where and whenever suits you. While fancy sports clothes aren't necessary either, it is a good idea to invest in a decent pair of trainers, which will make your first runs more comfortable and support your joints from impact.

While running can be a powerful tool for managing mental health, it's also a rigorous form of movement that won't and can't be enjoyed by everyone. For those who prefer to take their time and take in their surroundings, walking can be a better option.

Walking and hiking

Exercise doesn't need to make you feel like you're going to pass out to do you good. Walking can be very beneficial for your mind and body, as it increases blood flow and circulation to the brain and body, which in turn has a positive effect on your central nervous response system to reduce feelings of stress.

You can walk anywhere you like without special gear or a membership pass, but you'll likely experience

outside of the water. Swimming is more gentle on the body than high-impact activities such as running, as you use the resistance of the water to work your muscles and improve your aerobic fitness. It won't place so much impact on your joints and bones, but it will help you to stay flexible, so it's a great exercise for most people.

Dancing

Dancing is a very expressive, creative (and fun) type of movement, but it still shares similarities with many of the other exercises listed here. Dancing has a positive effect on mood and anxiety because it raises the heart rate (to boost endorphins), and focusing on a dance routine can certainly help us to divert our thoughts from job, family, and life stressors. It's usually a sociable activity, and we know that fostering positive social connections is another way to combat anxiety in the long term.

Yoga

While intense cardiovascular exercise such as running relies on the rush of endorphins to make us feel good, there's a growing mass of scientific evidence that also shows how moving our bodies slowly and thoughtfully – think yoga, pilates and tai chi – can help us to feel more calm and grounded.

Yoga encompasses some of the most common self-care and relaxation techniques, including breathwork, muscle relaxation, meditation, movement and even positive

an added emotional lift if you hike in a park, green space or natural environment. There's a reason that the Japanese have popularised the activity of forest bathing – trees and plants give out aerosols that can calm our mind. As if this wasn't enough, in wide open spaces humans can experience a rush of oxytocin, the love connection hormone that plays a role in human bonding.

On the subject of social bonding, there's no need to walk alone if you find it boring. Why not invite a neighbour, family member or friend to join you, or look after a dog and take them out with you? Walking combined with positive social interactions can improve anxiety and improve self-esteem – even if you just go for 30 minutes each time.

Swimming

Swimming is a great exercise for anxiety sufferers, as it forces you to breathe more deeply while also using all kinds of muscles — both small and large — that might usually get neglected

visualisation – it's no wonder that a regular yoga practice can reduce nerves and help you to be more present!

Thanks to online tutorials, classes and apps, yoga has become easier than ever before to access. Some people find group classes more spiritual, but if you want to try yoga at home, all you need is a basic mat and a quiet spot with enough room for stretching.

Weight lifting

Taking part in strength and resistance training (aka lifting heavy things) is also thought to have positive benefits for the body and mind. A few months of regular weight lifting has been shown to increase the size and structure of certain parts of the brain – those involved in regulating mood and mental function – and reduce anxiety and depression.

In some instances, weight training also requires mindfulness. Concentrating on lifting something in the right way requires great focus, forces you to pay attention to the present moment, and leaves you with little room to think about what's worrying you.

HOW MUCH EXERCISE SHOULD WE AIM TO DO?

Don't worry, you don't need to do a marathon every day!

The amount of exercise that experts recommend varies, but according to the National Health Service in the UK, "adults should do some type of physical activity every day" and "at least 150 minutes of moderate intensity activity or 75 minutes of vigorous intensity activity a week". Moderate activity includes brisk walking, dancing or even mowing the lawn, while running, riding a bike fast and sports like football and hockey all count as vigorous exercise. Of course, these guidelines are geared towards a baseline of physical rather than mental fitness, and the optimum amount of exercise for managing anxiety will depend on many factors, including your age and general health.

As a general rule of thumb, doing 30 minutes or more of exercise every day for five days could significantly reduce anxiety symptoms, but even small amounts of exercise – say, a 10-minute workout – may make a difference.

Remember that you'll only reap the anti-anxiety benefits of exercise if you can do it consistently over the long term, so focus on finding activities that you enjoy and will keep up – even when life gets extra-busy and stressful.

5950
STEPS

129

IS COMPETITION HEALTHY?

Community is one thing, competition is quite another

Setting goals can be a really helpful way to visualise intentions and help you to check in on your exercise progress. By all means sign up for a running race if you think it will help your motivation, but understand that competition isn't always a positive thing, and comparing yourself to others can be a total buzzkill. After all, it's harder to celebrate your first sweaty 5k run if your friend has just posted about her serene sunrise 10k.

It might sound corny, but we're all on our own journey. You're on a journey to discover more about yourself, your anxiety, to get fit, and to find

healthy ways of dealing with difficult feelings, sensations and emotions. Any goals you do set yourself should be specific, measurable, but most importantly, realistic.

Community is probably more powerful than competition when it comes to keeping up your exercise habits. Some people love the buzz of group exercise classes at the gym, knowing that they'll meet the same people each week for a session that's sociable and supportive. One example of a fantastic running community is Parkrun – a free, weekly 5km running event held every Saturday morning, in locations across

the world (www.parkrun.org.uk).

Run Talk Run is another weekly 5km gentle jog, designed to increase accessibility to mental health support through running and walking peer support groups (www.runtalkrun.com).

If exercising with others makes you feel more anxious and self-conscious – about the way you look, or that you aren't doing the right moves – that's okay too. Whether you go for a solo run or do a cardio class in your front room, exercise can also be a way to get some much-needed alone time and headspace.

"COMPARING YOURSELF TO OTHERS CAN BE A TOTAL BUZZKILL"

IS THERE SUCH A THING AS TOO MUCH EXERCISE?

Can you have too much of a good thing?

In the Western world, most of us aren't moving enough, but more exercise isn't always better and it is possible to have too much of a good thing. How much exercise is a very individualised question, but it's clear that, aside from physical injuries, over-exerting yourself can lead to feelings of exhaustion, and even exercise addiction. You certainly don't want to start worrying because you feel like you haven't exercised enough! When starting a new exercise programme, it's great to be enthusiastic and determined. But don't be tempted to do too much at once, or you could risk burning yourself out, then feel deflated when you don't reach the lofty goals that you've set for yourself. If you've decided to train for a half-marathon but have never run before, don't try to run 10 miles the first time.

Finding a schedule that works for you is so important – some people have more time first thing in the morning, whereas parents who need to get kids to school might find an afternoon workout more doable. There are loads of free training plans, apps and videos out there to help you, and having a guide can make the exercise easier to stick to. But remember that exercise should feel (on the whole) like something you *want* to do, rather than a punishment or a chore. Don't feel pressured to do more than you can because a workout needs to be ticked off, and definitely don't beat yourself up if you miss a few sessions.

"THANKS TO ONLINE TUTORIALS, CLASSES AND APPS, YOGA HAS BECOME EASIER THAN EVER BEFORE TO ACCESS"

YOGA FOR ANXIETY

The best yoga poses to reset your mind

TREE POSE (VRIKSASANA)

Balancing on one leg requires plenty of concentration, and this can help to divert attention away from a busy mind. When you're able to stand tall without wobbling, it makes you feel strong and steady, and in turn, perhaps more able to deal with your emotions.

CHILD'S POSE (BALASANA)

Often used as a resting pose in between challenging ones, Child's Pose stretches out the hips and the back muscles – areas where people often hold tension. It requires you to be still and, combined with deep breathing exercises, can help to reduce anxiety and fatigue.

BRIDGE POSE (SETU BANDHA SARVANGASANA)

Many yogis believe that inversion poses like this – where the head is below the heart – actually open up space around your heart and allow you to think more clearly. Fresh blood is sent to the brain, and the pose is thought to soothe the nervous system and reduce stress.

LEGS-UP-THE-WALL POSE (VIPARITA KARANI)

Take a few moments to do nothing in this pose. As it's very passive, it encourages you to sink into the floor and let go of any tension that you're holding. If you're tempted to fidget with your fingers, lay them out to your side or on your chest, and focus on your breathing.

HALF MOON POSE (ARDHA CHANDRASANA)

While beginners might find this pose a little tricky, it's known as a 'soothing' pose, providing a gentle and calming energy throughout the body. Often when we feel anxious we slouch or tighten ourselves up, whereas this pose opens up the body and encourages better posture.

MEDITATION & *THE BRAIN*

Training the brain to remain in the present moment can ease stress, reduce anxiety and even lower blood pressure. But how does it work?

WORDS LAURA MEARS

The English word 'meditation' comes from the Latin meditari, which means to think or to ponder. But the practice has its roots much further east than Rome. It originated in India as early as 4,000 years ago, before spreading eastwards to China and Japan, and westwards along the Silk Roads into Europe. Now, as brain scans begin to pinpoint the neurophysiology of meditative experiences, and research trials explore the effects meditation practices can have on our wellbeing, what began as a step on a spiritual path towards enlightenment is fast gaining a reputation as a panacea.

Neural rewiring for health and wellbeing

There are hundreds of different ways to practice meditation, but at their core, most use a form of focused awareness to calm and balance the mind. Though research is still in its early stages, trials are starting to reveal the difference that even a short meditation practice can make to health problems like depression, anxiety and insomnia.

It's important to note at this stage some of the challenges inherent in unpicking the effects of meditation on the mind. It is notoriously hard to design studies that truly measure subjective effects on mood and wellbeing, and due to the sheer number of different meditation practices, it's often difficult to compare the results from one trial to the next. The meditation experience of study participants can be variable, as can the length and duration of the practices they're asked to perform as part of each trial.

The absolute gold standard in medical research are randomised controlled trials. In these studies, participants are randomly separated into two groups: one receives the experimental treatment, while the other receives a different treatment or placebo as a 'control'. This enables researchers to really measure the difference that the experimental

"MEDITATION HELPS TO BOOST LIFESPAN, AND DECREASE ANXIETY"

LEARNING TO LET GO

Steve Harrison dedicated his life to the practice and teaching of yoga after a transformational experience with a yoga master. We asked him why learning to meditate is so hard, and what we can do to make it easier.

"I think for me the first thing to understand is that meditation is a state, rather than a practice. It's convenient to say 'I practice meditation', but it's not really the case. We can create an internal environment that is conducive to slip into a meditative state, but you can't actually do meditation because meditation is where doing ceases to happen."

....

WHY IS IT SO HARD TO LEARN TO GET INTO A MEDITATIVE STATE?

"In a modern world, it can be unrealistic to ask a mind to be able to focus. The obstacle that most people encounter almost straight away is their own bodies. Physical discomfort is, for a lot of people, a distraction from letting go into meditation. Sore knees, sore hips, backache... the body just keeps interfering. Focus techniques are an incredibly subtle device that require an immense amount of willpower. It can turn into a fight with ourselves to try to calm the mind when the body is not agreeing."

....

WHAT CAN WE DO TO MAKE IT EASIER?

"The ancients spent thousands of years devising ways to help people manoeuvre into a meditative state. It wasn't only the mind that was worked on. If you can do simple things to work with your body and your breathing, it will do a lot of work on the mind without the fight.
But the biggest thing for me, and I think the least spoken about, is our own psychology. Most of us are incredibly identified with our thoughts and our sense of individuality. In order to not constantly be pulled back into a thought stream about ourselves, we need to have a genuine interest in finding a space or an experience that's beyond our usual constructs of who we think ourselves to be.

"Ask yourself, how would it be if I just let go of myself for a moment? We don't disappear as a result of slipping into meditation, we expand."

treatment makes. But designing a control for meditation trials is tricky.

When researchers at Johns Hopkins University trawled through more than 18,500 meditation research studies in 2014, they found only 47 that met their strict criteria for proper study design and control. But within those 47 high-quality research papers, there were some clear psychological benefits: an eight-week meditation practice showed to improve symptoms of anxiety, depression, stress and pain.

This pattern of improvement in mental health problems is mirrored elsewhere in the meditation literature. Separate studies have found that meditation helps to boost lifespan, improve quality of life, lift mood and decrease anxiety for people with cancer. It helps to prevent relapse in people experiencing repeated bouts of depression. And, it can help people to cope with the symptoms of menopause and irritable bowel syndrome. Meditation also has positive effects on

"MEDITATION TECHNIQUES DRAW ATTENTION AWAY FROM REASONING AND JUDGING"

wellbeing in people without underlying health problems. It seems to improve working memory, focused attention and emotional regulation. In one study, participants listened to either a guided meditation or a language lesson. Then they were challenged with disturbing images. Those who had meditated were much quicker to recover from the emotional hit.

A quiet space and a comfortable seat

So how does meditation change the way our minds work? Many other tools that help us with emotional control usually work on the parts of the brain involved in conscious, rational thought. But meditation practices work differently. Rather than actively trying to control our thinking, meditation techniques train us to draw our attention away from the parts of the brain involved in reasoning and judging, and towards the more ancient structures that are involved in awareness of the present moment.

The brain constantly monitors incoming signals from the outside world, passing them through a structure just above the brainstem called the thalamus. It works like a comms relay, taking in sensory signals and forwarding them on to other parts of the brain for processing. Filtering this stream of information is an active process; we constantly and consciously have to choose what to focus on.

Our focus decisions are complicated by an additional stream of information, the sensations from inside our bodies. These are detected by the insula, the part of the brain responsible

TRY THIS AT HOME

Yoga teacher Steve Harrison shares a simple four-step meditation practice for beginners. This is an indirect method to do a lot of work on the mind without actually having to fight with the mind. Sit down, get comfortable, take some long, deep breaths, and create an environment inside in which the mind can actually start to focus.

BRING THE BODY INTO A COMFORTABLE SPACE

The one key is to be comfortable. Any form of physical movement or intuitive stretch can make sure that the body is as fluid as possible. Then ensure that the body is in the most conducive state to relax, without falling asleep. Sit on a chair, or in an armchair, but always ensure you have a straight spine in order to keep the brain-body connection alert.

SORT OUT YOUR BREATHING

If you're looking for the quickest way to create an equilibrium in your system, the breathing is the key. The state of the breathing reflects the state of the mind. If the breathing is agitated, the mind is agitated. If the breathing is calm, the mind will also become calm. Just gently start to control and deepen and steady the breathing in order to calm the mind without directly trying to control the mind.

FOCUS ON DEEP BREATHS

It's unrealistic to sit down and try to just watch your natural breath. Don't go too subtle too quickly – you will last seconds and then you'll be off. You'll have this constant ping-pong inside of returning to focus on your breath and then getting pulled back out again. So, deepen your breathing, because deep breathing is much easier to focus upon.

KEEP PRACTICING

You can slip into a meditative state by accident, but to slip into it at will requires lots of training. The mind that's not trained will generally be quite dissipated and unable to hold attention. But it's not necessary for the health benefits and the wellbeing to achieve the meditative state. Commit to regular, patient practice and just reach towards the point of meditation; there are a whole host of benefits that come with the journey.

for interoception, or internal self-awareness. It responds to feelings like pain, hunger and thirst, but also has a role in emotional awareness, and links in with other parts of the brain involved in attention.

Deciding what sensation to focus on falls to a wide circuit of connected brain regions called the 'salience network'. It uses the anterior insula (the internal sensor), the anterior cingulate cortex (the attention allocator) and the amygdala (the fear centre), to listen in on external and internal sensations, before then working out where we should put our focus. And it changes when we meditate.

Meditation practices almost always begin by taking a comfortable seat in a quiet space. This helps to minimise the internal and external sensations fighting for our attention and, over time, starts to change the way the salience network operates. During meditation, the thalamus remains active, still passing signals into the brain. But, with fewer distractions, the mind has room to focus in on sensations that often go unnoticed, like the feeling of the breath.

In experienced meditators, the connections in the internal-sensing insula change and strengthen, improving internal awareness, and grey matter in the attention-allocating anterior cingulate cortex increases, aiding focus and flexible thinking. Meanwhile, the prefrontal cortex,

THE MEDITATING BRAIN

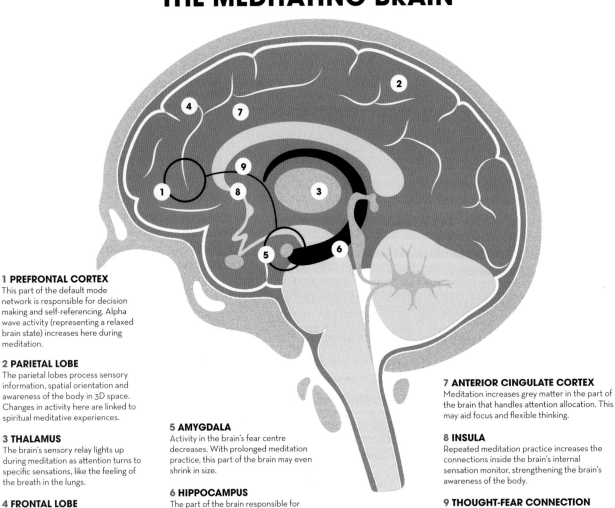

1 PREFRONTAL CORTEX
This part of the default mode network is responsible for decision making and self-referencing. Alpha wave activity (representing a relaxed brain state) increases here during meditation.

2 PARIETAL LOBE
The parietal lobes process sensory information, spatial orientation and awareness of the body in 3D space. Changes in activity here are linked to spiritual meditative experiences.

3 THALAMUS
The brain's sensory relay lights up during meditation as attention turns to specific sensations, like the feeling of the breath in the lungs.

4 FRONTAL LOBE
Activity in the large lobes at the front of the brain will increase as the meditator starts to consciously control the focus of their attention.

5 AMYGDALA
Activity in the brain's fear centre decreases. With prolonged meditation practice, this part of the brain may even shrink in size.

6 HIPPOCAMPUS
The part of the brain responsible for memory storage rewires in long-term meditators. The right hippocampus increases in size, affecting spatial memory and planning.

7 ANTERIOR CINGULATE CORTEX
Meditation increases grey matter in the part of the brain that handles attention allocation. This may aid focus and flexible thinking.

8 INSULA
Repeated meditation practice increases the connections inside the brain's internal sensation monitor, strengthening the brain's awareness of the body.

9 THOUGHT-FEAR CONNECTION
The link between the prefrontal cortex and the amygdala weakens with meditation practice, helping to stop fear and emotion interfering with attention and concentration.

which makes decisions, weakens its connection to the fear-inducing amygdala. One study found that after just eight weeks of meditation, the amygdala even started to shrink in size.

On a whole-brain scale, imaging studies have discovered even more widespread changes. Measures of white matter thickness show that meditation can boost connections in the front of the brain, which contains areas involved in attention and emotional regulation. Simultaneously, regular meditation seems to prune connections towards the back of the brain, in areas that are involved in self-referencing and egocentric processing.

Cutting out external interruptions and turning inwards during meditation rewires and reshapes the mind.

Focused attention in a wandering mind

Minimising distraction and internalising the mind is just one part of a meditation practice. The other major component is attention training. Many practices have a particular point of focus upon which to fix the attention; the breath, a word or maybe a sensation.

Depending on the focal point, different parts of the brain light up. Mantra meditations activate the auditory cortex. Moving meditations activate the motor cortex and cerebellum. And visual-focus meditations activate the visual cortex. But studies on blood flow in the brain have shown that, rather than direct the attention outside of the body, this kind of activity in a meditative state actually helps us to look inside.

Focusing on a single external sense, like sight, can activate the areas of the brain involved in internal sensing and, while this is happening, a part of the brain called the medial prefrontal cortex slows down.

The medial prefrontal cortex is part of the brain's 'default mode network',

the circuits responsible for our sense of self. The network lights up when we daydream, when we think about others, when we ruminate on the past, and when we project into the future. It tends to become active when we withdraw from the world into a resting state, but meditation practice changes how it operates.

Inexperienced meditators often notice that the mind tends to wander during meditation: that's the default mode network activating. It's the brain's way of planning, processing and thinking about itself, and it can run away with us when our senses are internalised. But, with practise, people seem to become better at noticing when the mind starts to wander, and can learn to gently bring it back into focus. And, with experience, the default mode network actually starts to slow down.

"WITH PRACTISE, PEOPLE SEEM TO BECOME BETTER AT NOTICING WHEN THE MIND STARTS TO WANDER"

A study of the brains of experienced versus novice meditators at Yale University found that repeated meditation practice re-tunes the default mode network. But rather than switch off, the network rewires. The connections in the network that control self-referencing and emotion weaken, while those involved in awareness of the present moment get stronger. This could explain why, in a meditative state, we are able to witness sensations, noticing the breath, the body or the thoughts without trying to interfere.

© Getty Images

Losing your self in the moment

The yogic scholar Patanjali described meditation more as a state of mind than an activity. The practices of removing distraction, internalising the thoughts and focusing the attention all serve to bring the mind to a place where it can enter an effortless meditative state. In this state, known in Sanskrit as dhyana, the sense of self dissolves, and the senses of space and time also fall away.

This type of experience is one of the most challenging to study because it is hard to conjure up on demand, but scans of Tibetan Buddhist meditators revealed that it might be associated with a decrease in activity in the parietal lobes. These brain regions handle the processing involved in picturing the body in 3D space, working out what's you and what isn't, and keeping track of time. Changes here seem to have the power to alter our perception of ourselves, not only during meditation, but also following other powerful out-of-body or loss-of-self experiences. In another study, which asked nuns to relive past spiritual experiences, the parietal lobes also showed shifting patterns of activity.

Body-mind connection and your physical health

Meditation has obvious effects on the mind, but can also induce changes to the body. Our psychology is powerfully linked to our physiology. Mental stress floods the body with

"MEDITATION NOT ONLY MAKES PEOPLE FEEL BETTER, BUT IT REDUCES PHYSICAL MARKERS OF STRESS"

a trio of fight or flight hormones: adrenaline, noradrenaline and cortisol. Their role is to prepare us to fight, freeze or flee. They raise the heart rate, quicken breathing and alter the metabolism.

Addressing feelings of stress using meditation can change the state of the body by transitioning the mind out of its 'fight or flight' mode and into its opposite 'rest and digest'. It flips off the sympathetic nervous system,

which governs the stress response, and flips on the parasympathetic nervous system, thereby easing the strain placed on the heart and lungs.

Studies examining meditation in people with anxiety, anger and high blood pressure have found that meditation not only makes people feel better, but it also reduces physical markers of stress. Stress hormones drop, inflammation markers fall, heart rate lowers, breathing slows down, and blood pressure decreases. For some, a single meditation session was enough to see a positive change.

Molecular studies suggest that the effects of meditation go deep into our physiology. In a small study at Harvard University, scientists found that 15 minutes of meditation every day for eight weeks could change patterns of gene expression. Our cells each carry an entire copy of the human genome, but they only need to use a handful of genes at any one time. So, they turn sets of genes on and off depending on what's happening around them. A regular meditation practice flipped the switch on 172 genes linked to the body clock, sugar metabolism and inflammation.

Beginning your own practice

Meditation is an active area of research and debate in the scientific community, and there is still much work to be done to understand how it affects the brain and how best to use it to improve health and wellbeing. But one of the best ways to learn more about the mental and physical impact of a regular practice is to experience it for yourself.

It can be difficult to know where to begin, but although there are hundreds of techniques, they can all lead to the same tranquil state. It's just a case of finding the methods that work for you. A good place to start is guided meditation. Allowing someone else to take you through your practice – whether at a class, or via an app, video or podcast – can help to keep you focused when your mind starts to wander. And you don't have to commit to a long session. Research suggests that just a short period of regular training is enough for noticeable effects. Be consistent, start small, and build slowly.

THE
GREAT
ESCAPE

Escapism is often denounced as a waste of time, but are there hidden benefits that are being overlooked?

WORDS EMMA GREEN

Everywhere we turn, we are bombarded by negativity. Whether it be from a 24-hour news cycle, divisive politics, economic worries or the pressure to balance an increasing workload with a personal life, it comes as little surprise that depression and anxiety cases are growing at an alarming rate. No wonder, then, that people are more desperate than ever to escape in order to maintain their own sanity.

This is not a new phenomenon either. Humans have immersed themselves in some form of escapist activity for thousands of years, whether it be through storytelling, song or live theatre. The only difference now is that technology provides us with a vast selection of choices to enjoy. Entire industries, such as Hollywood, are dedicated to catering to the public's insatiable need for escapism.

Escapism can be defined as anything that detaches somebody from their immediate reality, usually through an activity that involves imagination or entertainment. The most obvious forms of this include watching TV, scrolling through social media, playing games, shopping, reading and listening to music. Even activities that are a vital part of our daily existence, such as eating food, having sex and exercising, can become outlets for escapism.

So why is it important? Because escapism is a deep-seated human need. Imagination is what sets humans apart from animals. Without it, humans

> **"ESCAPISM IS A POWERFUL COPING MECHANISM FOR DEALING WITH NEGATIVE EMOTIONS SUCH AS ANXIETY AND SADNESS"**

would not be able to delve into their deeper consciousness, dream, re-live memories, create art or imagine new possibilities of being.

Escapism is also a powerful coping mechanism for dealing with negative emotions such as anxiety and sadness. It is a healthy outlet that temporarily removes us from an existence that can sometimes be too painful to bear. Without it, humanity would plunge into a persistent state of hopelessness and cynicism.

There is much comfort to be found in being able to escape into a world that provides a guarantee that things will turn out okay in the end and that the good

guys will always prevail. Reality, however, is unpredictable and offers no such promise.

That is not to say that escapism cannot be used as a form of catharsis. Watching sports or listening to music can provide us with a platform to vent our emotions in a safe space without risking harm to ourselves or others. Video games, in particular, enable us to discharge tensions without any real-life consequences, and to flush out negative emotions through fantasies of invincibility and theatrical outrage.

It is important to know when to engage with an emotion and when to ignore it. Emotions are often fleeting, and it can be more helpful to distract ourselves from a negative emotion rather than to focus on it. Emotions are notoriously cyclical in their nature, and sometimes ruminating on them can strengthen the emotion and end up making us feel worse.

By allowing ourselves to detach for

"EMOTIONS ARE NOTORIOUSLY CYCLICAL IN THEIR NATURE, AND SOMETIMES RUMINATING ON THEM CAN STRENGTHEN THE EMOTION AND MAKE US FEEL WORSE"

a while and shut off our emotions, we can give our minds a chance to reset and process matters more effectively. When we are overwhelmed, we can become blindsided by our problems and lose sight of the bigger picture. Indulging in some light-hearted escapism can remind us of the positive things in life. We are then better equipped to face reality from a fresher and more balanced perspective.

Escapism provides us with a boost of feel-good hormones such as serotonin and dopamine, an essential replenishment of the same neurochemicals that we lose when we are feeling stressed. This can help to dramatically improve mood and

keep anxiety and depression at bay. Escapism can also give us back a much-needed sense of control. By projecting ourselves through the personas we see on the big screen or in books, we can become the masters of our own domain and enjoy the sense of power, security and freedom that comes with it. Imagining ourselves as somebody who possesses something that we may lack, whether it be beauty, money or success, can be a powerful antidote against the disappointment of our own existence.

Furthermore, escapism can be a form of low-effort relaxation. Instead of viewing it as laziness or as a waste of time, we should look at it as 'refuelling'. According to Dr Michael Hurd, a

THE DOSE MAKES THE POISON

Escapism is a powerful coping method, but it can easily become a defence mechanism for protecting ourselves against feeling any discomfort at all. Too much escapism can lead to behavioural addictions, such as gambling or binge-eating.

It is important to differentiate between healthy escapism and avoidance. Positive escapism is a form of self-care, temporarily disengaging us from problems to re-energise, whereas avoidance can become a habitual way of ignoring our problems.

Avoidance is being so consumed by our chosen form of escapism that it becomes our primary purpose in life, rather than as a means of 'refuelling'. It can lead to problems at work, alienate us from our loved ones and cause us to stagnate in our personal growth.

We must recognise what it is we are trying to avoid through chronic escapism. It could be feelings of loneliness or boredom, or using it to compensate for a lack of interpersonal interaction.

According to Norwegian psychologist Frode Stenseng, two forms of escapism exist, depending on the motivation that lies behind each activity. Self-suppression (numbing activities such as abusing alcohol and drugs) comes from a desire to avoid unpleasant feelings, whereas engaging in self-expansion (activities such as meditation and creating art) are motivated by wanting to gain positive experiences and discover new aspects of the self.

It is vital that we strike the balance between using 'avoidant' coping strategies such as temporary distraction, and 'approach-oriented' techniques such as tackling challenges head on. Escapism is an important weapon in our wellbeing arsenal, but it is not the only one that we have to hand.

psychotherapist, and writer for the website 'The Daily Dose of Reason', refuelling "refers to things of secondary importance that we do in order to mentally or psychologically recharge our spirits so that we can better handle the primary commitments of career, relationships or family."

Comparing our brains to computers can help to override the guilt associated with taking time out for ourselves. Just as a computer can overheat, too much seriousness and negativity can fry our nervous systems. Without escapism, we would burn out much more easily.

The great thing about escapism is that there is little effort involved and the benefits are often immediate. Recent studies have shown that escapism can increase levels of restorative sleep, awareness and social connections while significantly reducing stress. Paradoxically, it can also boost our levels of productivity. Escapism can provide a much-needed respite for our brain by

encouraging easier thinking and a lower need for cognition. This means that when we do need to work hard, we can learn and focus better as our brains are not so exhausted.

Escapism essentially is about embracing 'mindlessness'. The concept of mindfulness and 'living in the present' has been all the rage in recent years, and while they are important for our mental health, so is the ability to switch off. Our society's obsession with achievement, success and busyness means that we can feel pressured to use our downtime constructively through goal-oriented pursuits such as learning a new hobby.

But trying to be productive all the time is not good for us. Allowing ourselves to engage in a 'mindless' or relaxing activity for no other purpose than to unwind activates our parasympathetic nervous system, which slows down our breathing and heart rate. This can reduce anxiety and stress by creating a sense of calm within us, which can help to reduce blood pressure and strengthen our immune system.

So the next time guilt creeps in about spending all day binge-watching Netflix, remember that 'practising mindlessness' is a crucial part of our mental wellbeing toolbox.

HOW TO GET TO SLEEP

Anxiety and insomnia are closely related. Here are some strategies to get a good night's sleep

WORDS EDOARDO ALBERT

Everyone reading this knows what it's like. It's half past two in the morning, you're staring up at the ceiling, wide awake, while all around you the world sleeps peacefully. Not being able to get to sleep is something that affects everyone occasionally. There is a peculiar loneliness to being the only person awake. The minutes stretch into hours, the night creeps past, and you turn and toss, trying to rest your mind while hoping that, finally, you will drop off.

In itself, this is perfectly normal. There are times when we all find it difficult to get to sleep. The difficulty is usually triggered by something that has happened or is going to happen: upsetting news, an important exam. Something stressful is filling our minds, keeping our thoughts in a churn and stopping the arrival of blessed sleep.

"INSOMNIA AND ANXIETY DISORDERS ARE INTIMATELY RELATED"

For most people, this is the experience of a night or a couple of nights, and then their sleep returns to normal. But for others, it is a regular occurrence; three, four, five nights a week. For some poor souls every night is a battle to get to sleep. The clinical name for this condition is insomnia and it will probably come as no surprise to learn that insomnia and anxiety disorders are intimately related.

Anxiety disorders are incredibly common. A 2013 study found that 8.2 million people in the UK suffered from anxiety during the year. The last two years, of pandemic and now war in Europe, have only exacerbated the situation. Every night there are thousands – if not millions – of people lying in bed, thoughts racing, worries churning, unable to get to sleep. Among the symptoms of the various anxiety disorders, an inability to get to sleep ranks very high. Most people suffering from an anxiety disorder will struggle to get to sleep, find themselves waking during the night, or wake in the morning but feel completely unrested.

Anxiety causes insomnia because people who are suffering from anxiety disorders are in a state of chronic, low-level stress. That means that the body continues to pump out stress hormones even when it's time for us to lie down and go to sleep. These hormones are the primers for action: the body, under stress, is preparing to fight or flee. Not surprisingly, it does not consider that dropping off to sleep is what we should be doing since it believes that danger is threatening.

Couple this with the mental hyperarousal that often accompanies chronic anxiety and you have a rather potent combination of factors that

"MOST PEOPLE SUFFERING FROM AN ANXIETY DISORDER WILL STRUGGLE TO GET TO SLEEP"

make it very difficult to fall asleep. To complete the picture, researchers have demonstrated that people with anxiety disorders also have higher sleep reactivity. Sleep reactivity is the degree to which exposure to stress affects sleeping patterns. People with high sleep reactivity suffer a marked worsening of sleep when stressed

AUTOGENIC TRAINING

Self-hypnosis to help you sleep

Autogenic training was first developed in the 1930s by the German psychiatrist Johannes Heinrich Schultz. He had noticed that subjects, when they were hypnotised, became very relaxed and later reported feeling subjective sensations of warmth and heaviness in their limbs while hypnotised. Schultz developed autogenic training as a form of self-hypnosis that could bring about relaxation without the need for a hypnotist, transferring agency to the subject.

It's a very simple procedure. You lie down somewhere quiet and dark. For help with sleeping, this will obviously be in bed. Then, you say quietly, "My left arm is heavy." You don't try to make your arm heavy, just state that it is and notice how the arm feels in response to your statement. Then say that your right arm is heavy, followed by both arms. Moving down the body, say that your left leg is heavy, then your right leg, then both legs. Moving to the torso, say, "My chest is heavy." Having completed that cycle, repeat it but this time say that your body is feeling warm. Studies have shown that autogenic training is effective in reducing anxiety levels, so doing this will help produce the calm necessary for sleep, while the training itself sets the body into a relaxed state allowing it to sleep. There are various slightly different formulations of what to say as well as apps that might be useful when first learning the technique.

GUIDED IMAGERY MEDITATION

Use your ears and follow the journey to sleep

Guided imagery is a meditation practice that, at least to start with, works by listening to a recording of someone leading you through a series of imaginings and gentle perception exercises to relax the body and mind in preparation for sleep. Another way of understanding guided imagery is to think of it as focused relaxation. It usually involves imagining a peaceful place or scenario. Some guided imagery journeys involve both. There has been considerable research showing the benefits of guided imagery meditations to improve anxiety levels and to help sleep.

If you want to try it yourself, search for guided imagery recordings. There are many of these available on YouTube and Spotify, and on apps including Calm and Headspace. When you've found a guided imagery meditation that you like, play the recording once you have finished your night-time routine and are lying in bed. It will normally begin with a breathing exercise, taking you into a calm, regular breath pattern. Then the person leading the guided imagery meditation may take you through an image journey, where you are asked to imagine a peaceful scene that the facilitator describes. The goal is to relax the mind and body and ease gently into sleep. Like everything, guided imagery meditations get easier and more effective with practice. While many people continue to use recordings, others create their own guided imagery journeys and use these to help them get to sleep.

when compared to those with low sleep reactivity.

But not only do anxiety disorders cause insomnia, the causal link works the other way round, too: insomnia causes anxiety. For people suffering from an anxiety disorder, the inability to sleep becomes a worry in itself, feeding the overall cycle of anxiety. Rather than bedtime being a chance to switch off from the worries of the day, it becomes a locus of worry in itself. To really round off this smorgasbord of woe, research indicates that people with anxiety disorders are particularly prone to suffering the ill effects of not getting enough sleep.

Sleep research has advanced hugely over the last 20 years or so. What all the research has shown is that a proper night's sleep really is extremely important for our health. At the most basic level, people who don't get enough sleep are at greater risk

"A PROPER NIGHT'S SLEEP REALLY IS EXTREMELY IMPORTANT FOR OUR HEALTH"

of dying than those who sleep well. Lack of sleep also leads to more risk of developing type-2 diabetes, as well as suffering from heart disease and obesity. A regular and sufficient sleep pattern boosts the immune system, improves the libido and protects from accidents.

That's just the physical benefits of sufficient sleep. The mental health benefits are just as remarkable. Insomnia is linked to dementia, both before its diagnosis and afterwards. But with respect to anxiety disorders, researchers have found that insomnia affects the amygdala. The amygdala

is one of the oldest and deepest parts of our brain. It evolved to deal with sudden danger and it is responsible for the fear reaction and the hormones that go with it. When the amygdala picks up on the fact that we are stressed, it interprets that as meaning we are in physical danger, so gets ready for fight or flight. Unfortunately, the amygdala is still stuck on the plains of Africa. It hasn't realised that the danger is, in fact, a presentation to a group of bored managers. It still gets us ready for action. As such, it is a key component of the brain driving the cycle of anxiety. The negative effects of insomnia on the amygdala therefore worsen its actions in the negative feedback loop that forms the cycle of anxiety, worsening an already fraught situation.

So it is clearly important to do everything we can to ensure a good night's sleep. One of the most important foundations for this is a

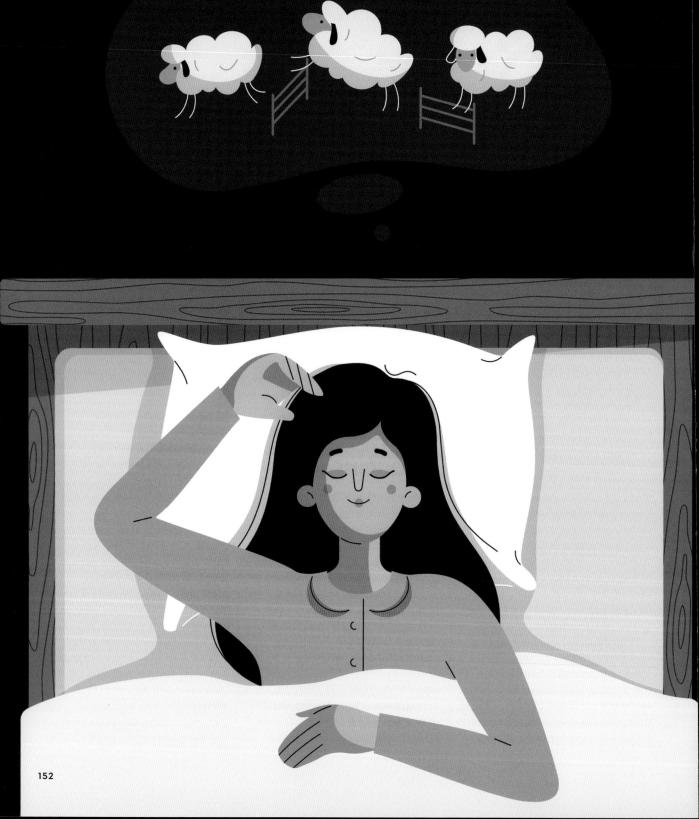

BODY SCAN MEDITATION

A guided meditation that focuses on the body rather than imagery

The body scan meditation is similar to the guided imagery meditation but here the focus is, as the name implies, upon the body rather than a peaceful imaginary scene. The aim of both meditations is to move the mind outwards from the anxiety churn to somewhere safe. By doing this, the guided meditations weaken the feedback loop that makes it particularly difficult to fall asleep when anxious, facilitating a peaceful night's sleep. As with guided imagery meditations, research has confirmed that body scan meditations can be helpful for many people.

To try body scan meditation, search for recordings on YouTube, Spotify or online. There are many out there. When you have found one that you like, incorporate it into your night-time routine and listen to the meditation as you settle down in your bed. As with most meditations, it will begin by guiding you through slow, calm, even breathing before moving on to the body scan. This does what it says: the facilitator will lead you on a journey through your body where you pay attention to various parts of the body, attending to their sensations with awareness but without judgement. The mind will wander off but simply bring it back to listening to the voice of the person guiding you. The aim is not to make your body feel anything in particular but simply to become aware of it in the present moment. Doing so moves your awareness out of your head and into your body, allowing it to relax towards falling off to sleep.

regular routine. Our bodies have a natural circadian rhythm by which they know when to go to sleep and when to wake up. Establishing a routine that aids and complements our body's natural sleep rhythm will help to produce a pattern of sound sleeping. To do this, we need to go to bed at the same time each night and get up at the same time each morning. The idea of sleep hours as some sort of bank from which you can withdraw one night and deposit the next does not work. We need to make sleep a regular habit, one into which the body will settle.

To facilitate the establishment of a good routine, it's helpful to abstain from caffeine for at least a few hours before bedtime as caffeine is a stimulant. Exercise during the day is excellent but again, the hours before bedtime should not be taken up with heavy workouts as these will prevent us getting off to sleep. Screens should be avoided for at least an hour before bedtime. The light that illuminates phone and computer screens acts on the wakefulness centres of our brain to rouse us, while social media and computer games are expressly designed to keep us involved in them, making it all too easy to stay up later than we intended. On the positive side, part of the bedtime routine can be doing things that are relaxing, such as taking a bath, meditating or reading. Breathing exercises to calm the body can also be helpful. However, even with the best routine in place, there will still be times when we can't get to sleep. Rather than lie in bed fretting about it, try sitting up and reading for a while. This will help reduce any anxiety that flared up from not being able to get to sleep and allow the body to reset itself. Then, when the body has calmed down and you are beginning to feel sleepy, repeat the final stage of your night-time routine and lie down again. Sleep will come. The trick is letting it.

HELP !

Caring for people suffering with anxiety

WORDS EDOARDO ALBERT

R ight, let's get one thing clear from the start. Saying, loudly and slowly, "Stop worrying and pull yourself together," won't help. People suffering from an anxiety disorder would love to stop worrying. Anxiety is not helping their life. In fact, it's making their lives very difficult. In the worst cases, it's making their lives hell. If they could stop worrying, they would. But they can't.

However, if you are family or a friend to someone suffering from an anxiety disorder, you will be all too well aware that the problem is not just limited to them. It affects you, too. In fact, it is possible that it is you, rather than the person suffering the anxiety disorder, who is the first to realise that there really is a problem. As we know,

despite the efforts to change this, there is still a stigma attached to admitting to having mental health difficulties. The person suffering from an anxiety disorder might not have realised that their worrying has gone past what is healthy. Or they may be perfectly well aware of this but be unable or unwilling to get help. As such, the family and friends of the person suffering an anxiety disorder might have a role right from the start in helping that person either recognise their difficulties or to seek help for those difficulties.

Of course, to do this you have to be able to tell where anxiety has moved beyond the everyday worries that afflict us all. There is an element of subjectivity to this. The Diagnostic and Statistical Manual of Mental Disorders, which is the psychiatric manual for mental disorders, states that for a diagnosis of generalised anxiety disorder (GAD) the patient's worry and anxiety must be 'clearly excessive'. What constitutes clearly excessive is left to the judgement of the psychiatrist. However, as a general rule of thumb, if anxiety is preventing someone living their life as they would want to live it, then the worry and anxiety is deemed to have become excessive.

> ## "THE EASIEST SYMPTOMS TO LOOK OUT FOR ARE OFTEN PHYSICAL SYMPTOMS"

Perhaps the easiest symptoms to look out for in someone you care about are the physical symptoms that often accompany an anxiety disorder. These include sweating, heart palpitations, quick breathing, nausea, headaches and restlessness. But just as important, and possibly even more debilitating, are the mental symptoms, which include, apart from excessive worrying, feelings of panic or being out of control, difficulty in concentrating, irritability, and feelings of guilt.

Should you realise that someone you care for is enduring symptoms like this, then it might be time to take the first step in helping them: asking him or her if they are having difficulties. Depending on the person, this is not an easy step to take and it needs to be approached with sensitivity. Before tackling them, consider when would be a good time to speak to them, where you can find that will be private, where

"AN IMPORTANT ASPECT OF SUPPORTING SOMEONE WITH ANXIETY IS NOT TO FACILITATE THEIR AVOIDANCE TACTICS"

the other person will feel comfortable and secure, and when you will both have time to talk.

It's possible that the person you're worried about won't want to talk with you right then. That does not matter. He or she might not have realised that there is a problem, or they might not be ready to talk. But opening the avenue is both a channel towards recognising the problem, if the recognition is lacking, and an invitation to talk further when ready. If they are not ready to talk, indicate that you will be happy to speak whenever they are ready and leave it until they are ready.

When the person is ready to talk, the first thing to do is listen. This might be the first time they have spoken about

what afflicts them. Let them speak. If the person is still trying to downplay the impact anxiety is having on their life, it might be worth pointing out the impact it is having on other people. The aim remains to support even if they become cross with you. Ultimately, you are trying to make sure they recognise the issue and, if its impact is great, seek help to address the problem.

An important aspect of supporting someone with anxiety is not to facilitate their avoidance tactics. The cycle of anxiety is built upon avoiding anxiety by finding some other behaviour to reduce anxiety rather than dealing with it directly. Facilitating this avoidance, while it might reduce anxiety in the short term, only serves to deepen the

habit groove and fix the cycle of anxiety more firmly. However, this does not mean forcing them to face their fears, and particularly not at this early stage of helping. The cycle of anxiety has probably deepened over a number of years: it won't stop from simply making them do what makes them anxious. Indeed, forcing the issue might provoke a much more intense anxiety attack.

Having opened lines of communication with the person suffering from anxiety, the next thing to do is ask them how they want you to support them. Do they want an occasional sounding board, someone to help in approaching medical professionals, someone to help break down a task into more manageable steps? Any of these can be useful but be guided by what the person wants. If they don't know, then you can suggest something, from seeking professional help through to some simple strategies to help them cope with their anxiety. It

"AVOIDING SOCIAL INTERACTIONS WILL ONLY SERVE TO MAKE THE ANXIETY WORSE IN THE LONG RUN"

won't hurt anyone to do some exercise and eat a better diet, so these would be good suggestions. Couple these with getting more sleep – most people with anxiety don't sleep enough, although in some cases that is because they suffer from insomnia – and cutting down on caffeine and alcohol, and you will have covered most of the straightforward pieces of advice that are helpful to pretty much everyone suffering from anxiety disorders.

Nevertheless, it is important to remember that, however much you have read about anxiety disorders and their treatment, you are not a professional psychologist. It's important not to attempt to take on that role. The most important thing a carer can do for someone suffering from an anxiety disorder is to be present and available for that person when he or she needs you.

Perhaps the most valuable way of being present and available is allowing the person with anxiety to be themselves when in anxiety's grip. Sometimes, it might be necessary for him or her to walk up and down the living room, or to leave the cinema in the middle of a film. They might need you to just sit there with them in silence until they are ready to speak or remind them to breathe when in the middle of a panic attack. Remember, they are the expert in their anxiety, you are an onlooker. Unless you have agreed a programme of interventions with the person and/or a therapist working with the person, listen to what they need and do it. Not being made

to feel as if they are mad is especially important for people suffering with anxiety disorders.

Even for people with chronic anxiety, there will be times when the anxiety lessens and things seem not so bad. It's helpful, at times like these, to have a shared pursuit that you can do with the person that you both like and that will be useful in reducing anxiety levels. Physical exercise is one possibility, from going running together to doing some gentle gardening. Other activities, such as yoga and involving mental tasks like jigsaw puzzles, can also be excellent ways to reduce anxiety levels. Anything that can help move the anxious person's focus from the internal theatre of their thoughts and feelings to the external world.

If the person you are caring for is particularly debilitated by anxiety, or if the anxiety is coupled with depression, then it might be necessary to help him or her with more of the practical side of living. Anxiety and depression are a common combination and, when severe, can lead to the person suffering from them withdrawing completely from the world. He or she will need help with basic living until help can be arranged – these are cases when professional assistance is necessary. However, while support will be necessary in such cases, try not to encourage dependency.

Even for less extreme forms of anxiety disorder, the constant stress that accompanies the disorder is very tiring. While your friend or spouse

might not be doing anything obviously physical to leave them so exhausted, the mental energy that goes into dealing with anxiety is enervating. So when he or she says that they don't have the energy to do something, they are telling the truth, not malingering. Accept that.

A common strand to the disorder is anxiety at the prospect of social situations. Indeed, one of the anxiety disorders is actually social anxiety disorder. In this case, the feelings of anxiety are linked to interacting with other people, with crippling worries about meeting strangers, social activities, fears of embarrassing yourself and the feeling of being watched and criticised. This is difficult to manage and enabling the anxiety by taking away social interactions with other people will only serve to make the anxiety worse in the long run. However, there are times when it is better to retreat rather than push on. One of the key skills of carers for people with anxiety is learning when to help the person push on a bit further and when to let them back off. Even if they do have to back down, remember to highlight any gain in what they did: they might have waited longer before cancelling the talk, they might have actually started speaking to a stranger at the party before deciding they had to leave. Any gains are good and should be highlighted.

Caring and supporting someone with an anxiety disorder is not easy. It requires tact, judgement, empathy and knowledge. But cultivating these qualities in yourself will serve you in many ways in your wider life and, with respect to your friend or relative, they will help immensely in making your support one of the planks upon which they can rest their recovery from this most debilitating of mental illnesses. It's a long journey and a hard one, but one worth making, both for yourself and the person you are helping along the road.

CARE FOR THE CARER

It's vital that carers allow time for themselves to recuperate

Caring is hard work. Yes, the person you are helping is suffering from the whips of the demons of mental anxiety, but watching someone suffer is a trial in itself. Even if the anxiety disorder is less serious, the presence of self required to truly help someone else is demanding and frequently exhausting. To prevent carer burnout and possible illness, it is important to give yourself breaks from the labour of looking after someone else. As such, it is important to set boundaries and limits on what you can do and to keep to these. After all, you won't be much use as a carer if you're ill yourself. Ideally, try and share the burdens of caring for the person with an anxiety disorder with family or friends, or seek professional help. You will not be less of a carer if you get in some back up every now and again. Another aspect of caring that is difficult is that you hear so much of the difficulties of the person you are caring for, but where do you unload the cargo of feelings that all this piles upon your own back? It would be very helpful to have someone else you can go to, to speak about the burden you are carrying and the effect it has on you. There are support organisations for people suffering from anxiety and their carers who will be glad to help.
These include:

Mind UK (0300 123 3393 / www.mind.org.uk)
-
National Alliance on Mental Illness USA (800-950-NAMI / www.nami.org)
-
SANE Australia (1800 18 7236 / www.sane.org)

GIVE YOUR
BRAIN
A
MICROBREAK

Just a few minutes' rest can help you reset and recharge. Here's how to refocus your energy quickly and effectively

WORDS DEBRA WATERS

We know that taking a break is good for us, both mentally and physically, but research has shown that employees benefit from mini breathers. "A series of recent studies on work breaks have argued that microbreaks are beneficial for wellbeing and productivity," says Professor Sooyeol Kim, who conducted one of the studies.

"RECENT STUDIES HAVE ARGUED THAT MICROBREAKS ARE BENEFICIAL FOR WELLBEING AND PRODUCTIVITY"

MICRO-HABITS

It's not just microbreaks that do us good. Micro-habits – that's a positive habit no more than a few moments long – can enhance our lives by empowering us to take small steps towards goals without overwhelming us. Here are some micro-habits to incorporate into your day.

TIDY
Make your bed – a tidy house is a tidy mind.

....

HYDRATE
Swap that first cup of tea or coffee for a glass of water.

....

ORGANISE
Write a daily to-do list in order of importance to help your day go smoothly.

....

BREATHE
Each time you unnecessarily reach for your phone (eg to check social media or play games), take deep, slow breaths for 30 seconds instead.

....

LEARN
Read a book, play the piano, write in your journal, or use a language app for just five minutes a day – eventually, you'll find yourself doing it for longer without it feeling like an effort.

"Taking microbreaks helps employees take respite and boost their energy." Yet microbreaks don't have to be restricted to our jobs – they can be taken at any time and in any place.

"Microbreaks are becoming more common and are increasingly fundamental for positive mental wellbeing," says life coach Kamran Bedi, author of *The Anxiety Antidote* (£12.99, Watkins). "Breaking up your day with one- to ten-minute breaks from work, tasks and always being on the go, can help relieve stress and anxiety, and overstimulation from the internet, social media and screen time."

This sounds encouraging, but you may be wondering how short breaks work as well as longer ones. "Microbreaks help because the brain can only focus on a specific activity for a certain length of time," says life coach Siân Winslade (**sianwinslade. com**). "We've been led to believe that multitasking is a good thing, whereas it just allows us to do two tasks at 50% capacity, doing neither of them well. We think that working through and finishing something is more important than how we're feeling, but if we think of our brains as batteries going into low power mode as our phones do, we use less brain power, go slower and become less bright and perky."

The beauty of microbreaks is that they don't take too much time, although you'll need to commit if you want to reap the benefits. "Returning to a simpler, slower pace of living with a ten-minute break can work wonders on your mind and body," says Kamran. "But incorporating a microbreak into your day-to-day comes through self-awareness and self-action."

To get started, set regular alarms or add some microbreaks to your daily 'to-do' list – like the ones we've suggested below – that way, you'll start to integrate them into your life. Trust us, you won't regret it.

Have a nap
Also known as a power nap, a short nap can give you as much energy as two cups of strong coffee, and the effects are longer-lasting, says Lisa Artis, deputy CEO at The Sleep Charity. "We'd usually recommend around 20 minutes to give the body a chance to recharge, but some people feel the effects from a micronap (ten minutes)," she says. "The best time to nap is the post-lunch lull (between 1pm and 3pm) – to avoid sleeping longer, set an alarm on your phone. An alternative is to hold a set of keys in your hand and lie down with your hand hanging. As you lose consciousness the keys will slip out of your grasp and wake you as they hit the floor."

Hydrate
Water is the basis of life, and even mild dehydration can adversely affect our blood pressure, body temperature and heart rate. Dr Kim recommends

"MICROBREAKS DON'T TAKE TOO MUCH TIME, BUT YOU MUST COMMIT TO REAP THE BENEFITS"

drinking water throughout the day, as does Siân. "Keeping a bottle of water nearby helps not only with your concentration and reaction time, but improves memory and mood, and reduces headaches, tiredness and anxiety," she says. Take frequent small sips rather than gulping down a whole glass – this enables the body to store more water because it won't overload the kidneys (and you'll need the toilet less).

Contrary to popular belief, the recommended two litres per day doesn't have to come just from water – black, green or herbal teas count, as does milk (especially fat-free) and even milky coffee.

Listen to Mozart

We know that music has the ability to affect our emotional state, but certain music can actually make us think more clearly. It's known as the Mozart Effect, and researchers found that listening to ten minutes of Mozart improved people's spatial-temporal reasoning* (the ability to organise and problem-solve). And another study** found that listening to Mozart for 25 minutes reduced blood pressure.

If you're not in the mood for classical, any music that means something to you can alter your mood. "Music is a great way to anchor particular emotions," says Zoe Thompson (**phoenixlifecoach. co.uk**). "I have a playlist that's calming, and one that's energising. Think about songs that make you feel a certain way and create your own playlists – just one or two tracks in five minutes can completely change your mood."

NEED SOME ENCOURAGEMENT?

Try the Pomodoro Technique

If you struggle to focus on tasks, then feel guilty taking breaks, you may need the Pomodoro Technique. For those who are wondering, it's named after the tomato-shaped kitchen timer the inventor, Francesco Cirillo, used to develop the method ('pomodoro' is Italian for 'tomato'). "The Pomodoro Technique is one of the most effective ways of taking a break," says Siân, who shows us how here:

· For every 25 minutes of focused time, take a five-minute break.
· *This can be repeated up to four times, then you'll need a longer break of 20-30 minutes.*
· One of the most important aspects of the Pomodoro Technique is that you move away from screens. Reading websites and checking emails taxes many of the same mental processes we use when working, compounding tiredness, so don't use your break to do anything that requires a screen.
· *Increase your heart rate and get 20 minutes' exercise every two hours by doing five minutes of movement every 25 minutes. Try jogging on the spot, lunges, squats or stretches.*
· For extra support, download a Pomodoro timer from the App store or Google Play.

Meditate

Sometimes, just a few minutes of alone time can be all you need to mentally regroup. And if you meditate you'll feel even better. "Whether you choose a guided meditation or you take some time out in a quiet room, meditation can help you focus on the present and be aware of your thoughts and feelings," says life coach Zoe. "This can bring a sense of calm and improve attention and focus." The Headspace app includes guided 'mini' meditations.

Try yoga

You don't need to commit to an hour's class – a few yogic breathing exercises and postures make an ideal microbreak.

"Yoga is a great way to bring you into the present moment and help you focus," says yoga teacher Danny Griffiths (**yoga-fit.co.uk**). "There are many variations, but a common thread is breathwork, known as pranayama. Bringing our attention to the breath and relearning to breathe slowly and fully can de-stress, which in turn helps with concentration and clarity. For example, alternate-nostril breathing such as nadi shodhana infuses the body with oxygen, calming and rejuvenating the nervous system."

You'll also benefit from a couple of postures – balancing postures, for instance, are particularly good for concentration. "Tree pose helps

> **"A CHANGE IS AS GOOD AS A REST, AND THAT INCLUDES EVEN THE SIMPLE ACTION OF STEPPING OUTDOORS"**

ground you, enhancing stability and calming the nervous system," says Danny. "While dancer's pose is another balancing posture that helps bring you into the present. This is great for getting over stress and anxiety, clearing the mind of useless thoughts, and improving blood circulation and endurance."

Step outside

A change is as good as a rest, and that includes even the simple action of stepping outdoors to look at a different view. "It's important to get outside, if only for a short period," says Siân. "Changing the environment allows for more stimulation of the brain and improves focus, reduces stress hormones, and improves mood."

And while you're outside, why not take a short walk? Even a quick stroll to the shops or around the garden is a microbreak well spent. "Walking raises the heart rate, therefore improving cardiovascular health, and helps you regulate deeper breathing, while the physical movement can also help release any stress or tension and re-energise you," says Zoe. "Getting outside also provides fresh air and very important vitamin D exposure, which aids our sleep and immune system."